To:

Lenwood Glenn Shriner

The 1960 Cecil Ryan, Jr.
Award for Achievement
in the field of Physics

Chipola Junior College

OUR NUCLEAR FUTURE

OUR NUCLEAR
FUTURE . . . *FACTS*

DANGERS AND OPPORTUNITIES

BY Edward Teller AND Albert L. Latter

CRITERION BOOKS · NEW YORK

Designed by Sidney Feinberg

MANUFACTURED IN THE UNITED STATES OF AMERICA
BY AMERICAN BOOK-STRATFORD PRESS, INC., NEW YORK

Preface

THIS BOOK has been written for the layman who has no knowledge about atoms, bombs and radioactivity. He knows that the world is made of atoms, that bombs might destroy it and that radioactivity could make it a place much less agreeable to live in.

We should like to give some advice about the use of the book: Each chapter can be read by itself. The chapters need not be taken in the order in which they are printed. To read them all will give a more complete understanding—and if you have time it is best to read them in the order they are arranged. Some of the earlier chapters perhaps overflow with facts. In some later chapters we wish that more facts were available. These latter the reader will probably understand and remember quite easily. He may not agree with all of their contents. On the other hand the more scientific chapters (II to VIII) will not be questioned but may be harder to read and to remember. It will be a help to keep this in mind: No chapter *follows* from another but most chapters are related and support some other part of the book.

Our knowledge about fallout is increasing rapidly. Some

questions which are raised in the book may already have been answered. With this added knowledge we might have been more quantitative in some of our statements. But we believe the main conclusions would not be altered.

This book was completed before the Sputniks. In their present form these have little to do with the subject of nuclear energy. However, to our mind, the urgency has become greater for the non-scientist to understand those parts of science and technology which may affect his safety and well-being, and the safety and well-being of his country. We hope that this book will contribute in some measure to such understanding.

Contents

List of Illustrations

A section of photographs will be found between pages 96 and 97.

OUR NUCLEAR FUTURE

CHAPTER I

The Need to Know

Our world is changing, and the change is becoming more rapid. The moving force behind this change is scientific discovery. All of us are deeply affected by the consequences of science. At the same time, very few understand the highly technical foundations of our civilization. In this situation it is natural that scientific and technical progress should create uneasiness and alarm.

Fear of what we do not know or do not understand has been with us in all ages. Man, knowing that his life will end, has often been prey to an even more terrible nightmare— the end of his whole world. In a scientific age most of the past terrors have turned out to be senseless chimeras. But one menace remains. It is the great and permanent unknown: what will we humans do to each other and to ourselves?

The worry about our own actions will continue. It may grow as our power over nature increases. Against this worry there exist two weapons: understanding and courage. Of the two, courage is more important but understanding must come first.

We are frequently alarmed by imaginary dangers, while

disregarding risks which are much more real. There should exist a close interaction between public opinion on the one hand and technical progress on the other. For this end an understanding of modern scientific developments is required. There is an increasingly urgent need to know. Little is done to satisfy this need. The opinion has gained ground that this need can in fact not be satisfied.

At the same time, more and more people believe that the scientists and technical people themselves are responsible for the changes which their ideas and inventions have brought about. The scientist is put in the position where his voice is heard, not only in the highly specialized fields in which he is an expert, but also in the much more general matters which are affected by his discoveries. The real source of important decisions in our country is the people. We believe that this is rightly so, and we believe that it is not proper if scientists take over any essential part of these decisions.

The responsibility of a technical man certainly includes two important functions. One is to explore nature and to find out the possible limits of our power over nature. The other is to explain what he has found in clear, simple, and straightforward terms, so that essential decisions can be made by all the people of our country—to whom the power of decision properly belongs, and whom the consequences of these decisions will ultimately affect.

To explain scientific and technical matters is not easy, and to become familiar with all science might actually be impossible. In the specialized field of physics there have been revolutionary developments in the twentieth century like the theory of relativity discovered by Einstein and the theory of the atom originated by Niels Bohr. These new discoveries are not easy to understand, and every good physicist has spent years of his life trying to get thoroughly acquainted with their meaning. All of us who have done so feel that we are well rewarded by the better understanding of nature which we have acquired. But it is not necessary to talk of these matters here.

What we have to discuss in this book is connected with parts of atomic and nuclear physics which are much more elementary. The facts which we shall present in a simple fashion are sufficient to give the reader an orientation in the seemingly bewildering fields of nuclear energy and atomic explosions.

We shall have to start by describing atoms and nuclei. These are rather small objects, but this circumstance need not particularly bother us; and it is not necessary to frighten ourselves with the idea that we are talking about "unimaginably" small objects. Our minds adapt themselves quite readily to new dimensions; and while we are talking about nuclei, we can temporarily forget that any bigger objects exist. Real difficulties arise only when science discovers laws which seem to contradict common sense. This does not happen frequently, and we shall not need to dwell upon such subjects.

The difficulties of explaining science are increased by the fact that scientists have developed a language of their own which they practice and perfect by talking to each other. One sometimes has the impression that they talk to each other exclusively. The authors feel that their own "native tongue" is this scientific language; this book is an effort at a translation.

A further difficulty is connected with the special subject: radioactivity. The great practical importance of this subject has dawned upon the public in connection with the explosion at Hiroshima. This was a frightening occasion, and the subsequent developments and prospects are no less frightening. It is not necessary that everything connected with nuclear explosions should be equally frightening; and it is important that we should approach the subject with an open mind and with as few emotions as is humanly possible. The emotions have their necessary place when we get to the stage in which we want to decide our actions. We suggest to the reader that he should delay this stage until the time when he has finished reading the book.

The greatest difficulty in discussing the radiation hazards arises because the working of living organisms is involved. Basically, we are in the dark about the question how such an organism works. We are equally in the dark about the question how such an organism is affected by radiation. It would therefore seem that we must remain in doubt whether or not radioactivity is dangerous, except for those cases where obvious damage has been done. Since the immediate effects of radioactivity are not perceived by our senses, we are faced with the thought of an invisible menace of unknown extent. Some of the harmful consequences may show up years later, and therefore even the absence of any observed damage will not reassure people.

Fortunately, our practical knowledge is by no means as deficient as these statements would suggest. Radioactivity, and processes similar to radioactivity, surround us and have surrounded our ancestors for as long as life has existed on earth. We do not know what life is, and we do not know in what detailed manner life is affected by radioactivity; but we have broadly based and certain knowledge that artificial radioactivity will produce similar effects to those produced by the natural background of radioactivity. This background, therefore, provides us with a yardstick to which all man-made contaminations can be compared.

There is a final obstacle to the explanation of matters connected with radioactivity. This is the secrecy which has been associated with the development of nuclear energy, and in particular with the military applications of nuclear energy. The arguments for keeping information concerning weapons secret are strong, proper, and generally understood. There is, however, no such strong argument, and in fact no possibility for secrecy connected with the widely dispersed radioactivity which originates from the weapons. In recognition of this fact, secrecy has been completely and properly removed from this field. It is not surprising that it took some time to do so. Administrative decisions have been involved, and these are never taken in a very great hurry.

Even though world-wide radioactive contamination has been since 1955 open to general scientific discussion, the time does not seem to have been sufficient to insure a wide dissemination and explanation of the results. There may also remain some lingering doubts whether all relevant information has been made available. In actual fact, the scientific information on this important topic is completely and freely available at the present time.

Information concerning the peaceful applications of nuclear energy is also completely and freely available. Even in the field of military applications, much of the essential information has been published.

We are therefore in a position to put before the reader the most important facts about the peaceful and military applications of nuclear energy—of the possible dangers and of the eventual benefits. If we do not succeed, we cannot blame either secrecy or the difficulty of the subject. It is true that the subject is involved, but only in the same way as are those subjects of everyday experience with which all of us have to struggle once in a while. No greater intellectual effort is needed than is involved in the understanding of the income tax form or the racing form, to mention two analogies of rather diverse emotional content. Many of the ideas will be unfamiliar, but they are not complex. Furthermore, their bearing on our safety, well-being, and the possible improvement of our lives is great. Therefore we hope that the reader will give as much of his attention to this matter as he is accustomed to devote to other subjects which are connected with his necessities or his amusement.

CHAPTER II

Atoms

ALL MATTER is composed of atoms, which are very tiny objects. We cannot see them because waves of light wash over them like ocean waves over a pebble. An atom is about as big in comparison to a human cell, which can be clearly seen under an ordinary microscope, as a human cell is in comparison to a billiard ball. Somewhat more precisely, a hundred million atoms laid side by side would be about an inch in length.

Despite its Greek name, which means indivisible, the atom is made up of parts. It consists of a central nucleus, which carries a positive electrical charge, around which one or more negatively charged electrons are distributed. One frequently hears of the electrons revolving in orbits around the nucleus, somewhat as the planets revolve around the sun in our own solar system. This is not quite a correct picture, however. For one thing the electrons are more elusive than the planets. They do not revolve in definite orbits as the planets do. Also the orbits are more delicate. One would destroy the atom by the attempt to find out precisely what the electron orbits are.

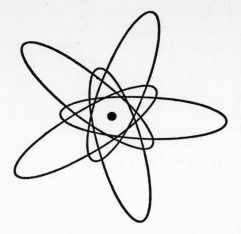

This is how an atom does *not* look. The electrons do not move along well-defined paths. It is more difficult to convey the idea of an atom by a picture than it is to make a drawing of last night's dream.

The planets do not fly away from the sun because of the gravitational attraction which the sun exerts. The electrons and the nucleus, however, are held together because positive and negative electrical charges attract each other. The gravitational attraction between the electrons and the nucleus is incredibly weak compared to the electrical attraction.

Most of the atom's weight comes from its nucleus. Even the lightest known nucleus weighs about 1840 times as much as an electron. In spite of this, the nucleus occupies only a tiny portion of the total volume of the atom. In fact, the nucleus is about as big in comparison to the whole atom as the atom is in comparison to the human cell. Twenty thousand nuclei laid side by side would be about equal in length to the diameter of the atom. If matter were composed of nothing but nuclei densely packed together, an object the size of a penny would weigh approximately forty million tons.

Later we are going to see that the size of the nucleus has a great effect upon the ways in which nuclei react with each other. For that very reason the size of the nucleus is a well-defined measurable quantity. It is much harder to say precisely what one means by the size of the electron. It seems acceptable to say that it is somewhat less than the size of the average nucleus. In any case it is certain that both the electrons and the nucleus are small compared to the size of the whole atom. Consequently, the atom must consist mostly of empty space. This means, of course, that when you look at solid matter, what is before your eyes is empty space with a slight addition of real substance. What lends strength to solids is the interplay of electric attractions and repulsions inside atoms and between atoms.

When a charged particle, such as an electron or a nucleus, happens to move through solid matter, it is constantly acted on by large electric forces. To such a particle matter does not seem to be very transparent. But if there were such a thing as an electrically neutral particle, comparable in size to the nucleus, it would be able to move around freely inside matter, without experiencing electric forces, and only now and again bumping into a nucleus or maybe an electron. As a matter of fact, there is such a particle and it can pass right through an inch or two of solid matter without bumping into anything. Later on in this book we shall be very interested in this particle, which is called a neutron.

Although the electrons and the nucleus are charged particles, the atom as a whole is electrically neutral; this means that the positive charge of the nucleus must be equal in magnitude to the total charge of all the negative electrons. All electrons have precisely the same charge, which is the smallest charge that has ever been observed. What is particularly strange and not yet explained is the fact that all other charges are as big as the electron charge, or twice as big, or three times as big, or a million times as big. But we never find a charge which, expressed in terms of the electron charge, is fractional. No object ever carries three and a half electron charges. The electron charge therefore may be used conveniently as a standard unit of charge.

Every atom can be distinguished by the charge of its nucleus. The simplest atom one can imagine would clearly be one with a single electron revolving around a nucleus having one unit of positive charge. Such an atom exists and is called hydrogen. An atom with a nucleus of charge two and two electrons revolving around it, is called helium; three, lithium . . . six, seven, eight; carbon, nitrogen, oxygen . . . 92, uranium. Atoms with almost all charges from one to 92 are found in nature, and practically none above 92 are found. Some odd charges—43, 61, 85, and 87—are missing. The reason for these missing atoms is connected with the properties of the nucleus. The nucleus will soon become our main object of interest.

The most surprising fact about atoms is their similarity, indeed their identical behavior. If two atoms have the same kind of nucleus and have the same number of electrons revolving around these nuclei, then these two atoms are apt to be encountered in a condition which is most precisely the same for the two. One could imagine that the various component parts of the atom would be arranged in different ways and found in different states of motion, in a variety without limit. Whence the complete similarity? The answer to this question is not only most surprising, but it is even in apparent contradiction to common sense. For this very reason it is difficult to explain. The hardest things to understand are not those which are complicated but those which are unexpected.

Fortunately for our purpose we need not go into this more intricate portion of atomic physics. It is sufficient to say that there is one arrangement or pattern of motion of the electrons which is preferred and which leads to the greatest stability of the atom. If the electrons are in this particular state of motion, which is called the ground state, they have less energy than they would have if they were in any other state of motion. There are other less stable, but not less sharply defined, states of atoms which we call "excited" states. When an atom is in such an excited state, it tends to be unstable and tries to get into the ground state as soon as possible. Since the ground state contains less energy than any other state, the atom must release energy in the process of adjustment. The released energy manifests itself in the form of electromagnetic radiation—often as a little pulse of visible light. The color of this light depends upon the amount of energy released, going progressively through the rainbow from red toward blue as the amount of energy increases.

There are very few states in which the excitation energy is small. But of strongly excited states there is a great abundance. In the region of this high excitation small additional changes are possible. Thus we approach a situation more in accordance with experience and common sense: the pattern of motion can be changed by any small amount.

The description we have just given is of course incomplete. We must avoid here the crucial questions why only some patterns of motion are possible, why one lowest level is stable and why the electrons never descend into decreasing states of energy, following the attraction of the nucleus. At the same time one should emphasize that a complete explanation of these facts has been given. This explanation makes precise predictions about many of the properties of matter, and we can have complete confidence that, but for the involved mathematical procedure, all ordinary properties of materials could be precisely predicted. The atom has been explained as completely as Newton has explained the motion of planets.

To form an idea what an atom is or why two atoms of, let us say, hydrogen are precisely the same, it is not necessary to search for intricate reasons or deep meanings. Two atoms of the same kind are alike as two pawns are for the chess player, except for one little point: in the case of the pawns we do not *care* about the difference; in the case of the atoms there *is* no difference. This is a simple statement and it honestly describes a simple situation. The beauty of science is due to the fact that the correct answers to our most interesting questions have turned out to be surprising by their simplicity.

In order to understand an atom one must consider the distribution of electrons around one nucleus. In order to understand a molecule one has to consider the distribution of electrons around two or more nuclei. The *chemical* behavior of an atom is the manner in which it interacts with other atoms, and that means the precise way in which the electrons rearrange themselves when two or more atoms approach each other. The interaction between atoms occurs mainly between their outermost electrons. It may happen that two quite different atoms, containing nuclei of different charges and different numbers of electrons, may nevertheless be similar in the structure of their outermost electrons. In this case the two atoms exhibit similar chemical properties. Examples are lithium with charge 3 and sodium with charge 11; also helium, charge 2 and neon, charge 10. A most important example for our purpose is the set of three chemically similar atoms: calcium, charge 20, strontium, charge 38; and radium, charge 88.

When two or more atoms approach each other, whether they are similar or different, their electrons—particularly the outermost ones—find new states of motion instead of those that were available to them when there was only one nucleus in the vicinity. It may now happen that amongst these new states of motion there are some that are even more stable than the state of the separated atoms. In this event the atoms will tend to stick together, and the electrons will adopt whatever new state of motion now corresponds to maximum stability. The composite system of the atoms is called a molecule, and its state of maximum stability, the ground state of the molecule.

There are atoms of particularly great stability which cannot increase their stability by combining with other atoms. Examples are helium, neon, and argon. These atoms tend to remain single, retain their independent motion in a rather "permanent" gaseous state, and are generally unsociable. They are called therefore the noble gases.[1]

An especially simple example of the formation of a molecule is the combining of sodium and chlorine to form ordinary table salt. The sodium atom happens to have a rather loosely bound outer electron. The chlorine atom possesses a convenient niche for an extra electron. Consequently the energy spent in prying the outer electron loose from the sodium atom is largely repaid by adding it to the chlorine atom. The remaining sodium "atom," deprived of one of its electrons, now has a net positive charge.[2] The chlorine "atom" with its extra electron has a net negative charge. The two "atoms" therefore attract each other to make a molecule of sodium chloride. Actually matter will continue to aggregate. A great number of positive sodium "atoms" and negative chlorine "atoms" will arrange themselves into a beautiful and regular lattice which is the sodium chloride crystal.

The simplest molecule which does not tend to grow into a bigger aggregate is made up of two hydrogen atoms. Around two hydrogen nuclei a particularly stable pattern of two electrons can be formed. Because of this fact hydrogen atoms associate pairwise so that this pattern should become possible.

The ways in which atoms can be joined are incredibly manifold. They can form metals in which the outer electrons

[1] The word "noble" is perhaps a misnomer—these atoms do not even seek the company of each other.

[2] Quotes are put around the word atom because, having lost one of its electrons, it is no longer an ordinary neutral atom in its ground state.

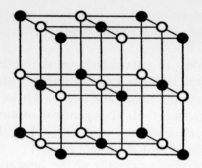

Arrangement of sodium and chlorine "atoms" in a crystal of common salt.

roam freely and carry electric currents with the greatest of ease. They can form liquids in which atoms or molecules are tied together in a loose and disorderly fashion. They can move independently making occasional encounters, which is what happens in a gas. And they can form long spiraling molecules where groups of atoms are strung together without an apparent simple order, but in a way which is somehow related to the processes of life.

We all know in how many forms matter can appear and how changeable these forms are. That the stone and the spray, the air and an insect, and even the human brain should be composed of the same few kinds of atoms, and that these atoms should be subject to laws which are subtle and simple and precisely described—this certainly is the most remarkable fact that we have learned since Newton proved that the same science applies to the earth and in the heavens.

CHAPTER III

Nuclei

Up to now we have regarded atoms as being divisible into electrons and nuclei. Electrons and nuclei, however, we have regarded as indivisible entities. This point of view is perfectly adequate to account for all the facts of chemistry and most of the facts of physics. Even in physics, it has not been necessary to ascribe an internal structure to the electron.[1] The electron is a truly elementary particle in this sense. However, to understand some physical phenomena, and radioactivity is one of these, it is necessary to recognize that the nucleus is not indivisible but consists of parts. The parts of the nucleus are called protons and neutrons.

The simple statements of the previous chapter apply to these smaller particles also. All electrons are equal—precisely equal. All protons are equal and all neutrons are equal. There are methods which would have shown up exceedingly small differences between these particles. No such differences have been discovered. As far as we know these particles are *always* the same. We cannot pour energy into them and excite them as was the case with the atoms. When we come to

[1] Yet.

consider these small particles, the complex structure of the world has an end. Instead what we find is simple.

A proton and a neutron have almost exactly the same weight. The proton has one unit of positive charge, which means that its charge is the same as that of the electron except that it is opposite in sign. The neutron, as its name implies, is an electrically neutral particle. Hence the charge of the nucleus is equal to the number of protons it contains, and is independent of the number of neutrons. The weight of the nucleus, however, taking the proton (or the neutron) as a unit of weight, is equal to the number of protons *plus* the number of neutrons.

Imagine that we have two atoms whose nuclei have the same number of protons but a different number of neutrons. Such atoms exist in nature and are called isotopes. The point about these isotopes is that since they have the same number of protons, they have the same nuclear charge, the same electron structures, and hence they have almost the same chemical properties. Their nuclei have somewhat different volumes. But the nucleus is small in any case. It is almost as though we tried to look for the difference between nothing and twice-nothing. The difference in the weights of isotopes due to the difference in their numbers of neutrons, has only a negligible influence on their chemical behavior. An important consequence of this fact is that molecules which differ only in that one isotope has been substituted for another are biologically indistinguishable. They taste the same and smell the same. They are ingested in our bodies in the same way, and they are deposited or excreted in the same way.

The simplest isotopes are the isotopes of hydrogen. Most of the hydrogen atoms we find in nature have a nucleus which is a single proton. This is the common hydrogen or light hydrogen. A few hydrogen atoms, however, have nuclei which consist of a proton and a neutron. This is the heavy hydrogen, found in heavy water. In all natural sources of water these two kinds of hydrogen are mixed in a ratio which is practically the same for every sample. The electron circulating around the nucleus behaves almost exactly the same way whether the extra neutron is present or not. On the state of that electron depend most properties of the atom and the molecules which contain it. Of course, heavy hydrogen has twice the weight of common hydrogen, and heavy water is somewhat more dense than light water. But otherwise there is little difference.

The story of the discovery of the hydrogen isotopes is amusing. About half a century ago—before the discovery of any isotope—two scientists tried to measure the density of water. They purified the water by boiling it and condensing the vapor. But the more they purified, the lighter it became —slightly but perceptibly. Finally they gave up: water seemed to have no density!

What really happened was this: Light water boils a little bit more easily than heavy water. Without realizing it, these scientists had started to separate isotopes.

Many years later Harold Urey—on the basis of some mistaken experiments of other people—concluded that heavy hydrogen must exist. He looked for it and found it, but found much less than he had expected. There was so little heavy hydrogen that on the basis of correct experiments Urey never would have guessed its presence. It seems that an unfounded idea is much more fruitful than the absence of an idea.

Almost all naturally occurring elements are found to consist of more than one isotope. Uranium, for example, is composed mainly of two, one having 143 neutrons and the other having 146. Since both of these isotopes have 92 protons, their weights are $92 + 143 = 235$ and $92 + 146 = 238$ respectively. It is customary to refer to these isotopes as U^{235} and U^{238}. The U^{235}, which is valuable in atomic reactors and in the manufacture of atomic bombs, is comparatively rare, occurring as only one part in 140 of natural uranium. The separation of this rare isotope from the common 238 was one of the major undertakings of the two billion dollar Manhattan Project during World War II.

We come now to a most important question, one that will lead us to the idea of radioactivity: What is it that determines which isotopes a given element will have? For example, uranium has isotopes weighing 235 and 238. Small amounts of U^{234} and U^{236} are also found in nature. Why do we not find U^{232}, U^{233}, U^{237} or U^{239}? Evidently only certain numbers of neutrons will hang together with 92 protons.

Consider another example, this time of the lightest known element, hydrogen. We have already mentioned two isotopes of hydrogen: light hydrogen with weight 1 (symbolized H^1), having a nucleus consisting of a single proton and no neutrons, and heavy hydrogen (also called deuterium) of weight 2 (H^2), having one proton and one neutron. The latter isotope occurs as only about one part in 5,000 of natural hydrogen. There is also a slight trace of tritium (H^3), having one proton and two neutrons. But here the sequence stops. What has happened to H^4, H^5, H^6, etc?

This question is related to the earlier one: why there are no atoms in nature of charge 43, 61, 85, and 87, and why there are none with charges greater than 92. To answer these questions requires a little knowledge about the laws which govern the motion of neutrons and protons within the nucleus, and the nature of the forces which are exerted by a neutron on a neutron, a neutron on a proton, and a proton on a proton.

The motion of neutrons and protons within the nucleus is governed by the same laws which govern the motion of electrons within the atom. For both the nucleus and the atom there is a ground state of motion which has more stability (less energy) than any other state. Of course the arrangement and motion of electrons in the atom depend not only on this general rule but also on the specifically electrical nature of the forces which act between the electrons and the nucleus. In the same way the arrangement and motion of the neutrons and protons within the nucleus depend upon the nature of the forces which act between neutrons and protons.

These forces are definitely not of gravitational origin. Gravitational attraction is extremely weak compared to the attraction between neutrons and protons, and is utterly negligible in the realm of nuclear phenomena. Neither can the nuclear forces be electrical in origin. The neutrons are electrically neutral; and the protons actually repel each other by virtue of their electrical charge. The nuclear forces are something entirely new. They are the strongest forces yet encountered, and they are without a counterpart in the macroscopic world.

Nuclear forces are not yet completely understood. But to understand nuclear stability we need to know only one peculiar fact governing the behavior of neutrons and protons (and incidentally also electrons): They want to be different. To each particle a state or pattern of motion can be assigned. When any two neutrons are compared, their pattern of motion must be essentially different. The same holds for any two protons. A neutron and a proton, however, may be found in similar patterns since they differ anyway in their charge.

Now among the possible patterns of motion some have lower and some have higher energies. Individual neutrons and protons will first occupy the lowest energy states, in accordance with the rule of least energy for maximum stability. Then the demand for a difference will force subsequent particles into patterns of higher and higher energies.

Since a neutron does not exclude a proton from being in the same pattern, the lowest energy state may be occupied simultaneously by one neutron and one proton.[1] If another neutron or proton is added, it must be put into the next state of higher energy. For this reason we would expect that nuclei are most stable when they contain an equal or nearly equal number of neutrons and protons. For nuclei which are not too heavy, this is indeed the case. For example, nitrogen, which has seven protons, has two stable isotopes, N^{14} and N^{15}, with seven and eight neutrons respectively. For heavy nuclei, however, the situation is a little different.

The nuclear force between neutrons and protons acts only over a very short range—the particles must almost be in contact with each other in order to experience a sizeable attraction. Consequently a neutron or a proton interacts only with its immediate neighbors in the nucleus. The electrical repulsion between the protons, however, acts over a much longer range. A proton is repelled by all the other protons in the nucleus. For heavy nuclei this repulsion is sufficient to reduce the number of protons relative to the number of neutrons. Lead, for example, with 82 protons, has four stable isotopes, with 122, 124, 125, and 126 neutrons.

We have said that seven protons will combine stably with seven or eight neutrons. What happens if seven protons are combined with six or nine neutrons (to make N^{13} or N^{16})? Our rule does not prevent them from sticking together; it says only that these combinations would be *more* stable if a proton could be converted into a neutron (in the case of six) or a neutron into a proton (in the case of nine).

Actually seven protons and nine neutrons *do* stick together, but such a nucleus is not stable and does not continue to exist indefinitely. The reason is quite simple and a little surpris-

1 Actually the same state may be occupied by two neutrons and two protons. The reason is that neutrons and protons are magnetic particles with a north and a south pole. Consequently the demand for a difference can be satisfied by having one neutron (or proton) with its north pole pointing up and another with its north pole pointing down.

ing: The conversion of a neutron into a proton is actually a physically realizable process, and furthermore it releases some energy. Similarly a nucleus containing seven protons and six neutrons will have an existence of only finite duration because the conversion of a proton into a neutron can also occur. Of course the proton is charged and the neutron is not. What happens to the charge during these transformations? Actually the neutron is transformed, not into a proton, but into a proton plus an electron. The proton is transformed likewise into a neutron plus something else. This something else is called a positron and is identical with the electron in every respect except in having a positive instead of a negative charge.

The changes just described occur spontaneously. They are examples of radioactivity. More specifically they are called "beta decay" processes because an electron (or a positron) when emitted by a nucleus is called a beta ray. Such beta-radioactive substances are produced whenever nuclear energy is used in an explosion or in a power plant. Many of the difficulties and worries concerning nuclear energy are connected with these beta activities. We shall be concerned with them often as harmful, sometimes as helpful agents.

When a neutron is converted into a proton and an electron inside a nucleus, the electron escapes immediately, but the proton remains in the nucleus. Similarly, when a proton is converted into a neutron and a positron, the positron escapes and the neutron remains in the nucleus. Since the electron and the positron have a negligible weight compared to a proton or a neutron, the process of beta decay leaves the weight of the nucleus nearly unchanged. Since the electron and the positron are charged, the process of beta decay increases or decreases the charge of the nucleus by one unit.

After beta decay a nitrogen nucleus with seven protons and six neutrons (N^{13}) becomes a nucleus with six protons and seven neutrons—carbon with weight 13 (C^{13}), which is a stable combination. Similarly a nitrogen nucleus with seven protons and nine neutrons (N^{16}) becomes a nucleus with eight protons and eight neutrons, oxygen with weight 16 (O^{16}), which is ordinary stable oxygen.

Sometimes after a beta decay the residual nucleus finds itself with a "correct" number of neutrons and protons but with an excess of energy. That is, the residual nucleus is not in its ground state but is excited. This happens in about two thirds of the known cases of beta decay. It happens, for instance, when N^{16} decays to O^{16}.

In this situation the excited nucleus will behave like an excited atom. An excited atom, the reader will recall, gets rid of its excess energy by emitting electromagnetic radiation, usually visible or near-visible light. The excited nucleus will get rid of its excess energy in exactly the same way. The only difference is that the amount of energy carried by the electromagnetic radiation from the nucleus is approximately a million times greater than that carried by the electromagnetic radiation from the atom—an indication of the large quantity of energy stored up inside the nucleus. Such energetic electromagnetic radiation emanating from a nucleus is usually called a gamma ray. Gamma-ray emission, or gamma decay, like beta decay, is an energy-releasing process which changes an unstable nucleus into a stable one, or at least into a more stable one. More generally, any spontaneous energy-releasing process (which tends to stabilize the nucleus) is called radioactivity. Beta and gamma decay are two examples. Later on we shall consider a third example called alpha decay. An alpha particle is the nucleus of the helium atom and consists of two neutrons and two protons.

The decay of a neutron and the decay of a proton appear to be quite analogous processes. Actually there is an important difference between the two. A free neutron—one not confined inside a nucleus—will decay into a proton and an electron; but a free proton will not decay into a neutron and a positron. This difference is due to the fact that the proton has a slightly lower weight than the neutron and therefore has less energy. For the proton to decay, it must be inside a nucleus where it can absorb some energy from the other protons and neutrons.

One sometimes finds pairs of nuclei which could transform into each other by a proton-neutron (or neutron-proton) conversion; nevertheless neither of these conversions can occur in the way we have just described. The reason is that in a proton-neutron or neutron-proton conversion an additional electron or positron has to be emitted. Now according to Einstein the mass of the electron or positron corresponds to some energy $(E = mc^2)$, and it may happen that neither the neutron-proton transformation or the proton-neutron transformation releases enough energy to make an electron or a positron.

In such cases one of the innermost electrons of the atom may combine with a proton to make a neutron. Such an electron-capture process will always release energy provided that the reverse process—the transformation of a neutron into a proton and an electron—is connected with an energy deficit. Thus, excluding the possibility of a really exact coincidence of two energies, one of the two transformations from neutron to proton or proton to neutron will always be possible.

It is one of the most firmly established laws of nature that energy is always conserved. One would therefore expect that the energy of a beta ray would be exactly equal to the difference between the energy of the nucleus before the beta decay and the energy of the nucleus after the beta decay. As a matter of fact the energy of a beta ray is found never to be as great as this amount. Frequently it is much less. Some of the energy has apparently disappeared and the suspicion has been voiced that energy may not be conserved after all. It has turned out, however, that the missing energy is smuggled out of the nucleus, and the smuggler (who has only recently been caught) is called the neutrino.

The neutrino is an electrically neutral particle, like the neutron, but its weight, like the weight of a ray of light, is equal to zero. Like such a ray, it moves with the velocity of light.

The energy released by the nucleus in the beta-decay process is shared more or less equally between the neutrino and the beta ray. We shall see later that the electron gives rise to a number of effects. Some of these are harmful. The neutrino, however, is not in the least dangerous. Like an ideal smuggler it passes unnoticed and practically without a trace. It interacts so slightly with matter that several billion of them may go right through the whole sphere of our earth before a single collision occurs.

Very recently this strange little particle has upset one of our most unquestioned concepts about symmetry. We have always believed that nature made no distinction between her right hand and her left hand; that for every natural process that exists, there exists also the mirror image of this process. The neutrino, however, is an exception. It has a definite symmetry, like a screw.[2] This fact may turn out to be most important in the development of science. It has no bearing, however, on the questions to be discussed in this book.

Neutrinos reach us from some distant and hidden places like the interior of our sun and of exploding stars. It may become possible to use neutrinos as messengers to reveal the kind of nuclear reactions from which the energy of the stars is derived.

[2] It seems that neutrinos emitted in the company of electrons have the symmetry of a right screw; those emitted together with a positron have the symmetry of a left screw.

Neutrinos are also emitted every time we release some nuclear energy. Among all the remarkable practical consequences of nuclear energy, the neutrinos have a unique distinction: they are never useful, and they are never harmful. They have not even been suspected of any mischief.

CHAPTER IV

The Law of Radioactive Decay

A RADIOACTIVE nucleus is one that will eventually disintegrate and release some energy. But when?

One might imagine that a radioactive nucleus would begin to "age" from the moment of its birth, and that after the passage of a predetermined time, the disintegration process would take place. This is how radioactivity *might* work in a deterministic universe. What actually happens to a radioactive nucleus, however, is much more interesting.

At any instant of its life, the radioactive nucleus has some probability of disintegrating in the next second. This probability is unaffected by its age. No matter how long the nucleus has lived, its chance of disintegrating in the next second is always the same. It is as if a game of roulette were being played. The wheel spins, and if its number comes up, the nucleus disintegrates in the first second. If not, the wheel spins again. Each time the wheel spins there is some probability of its number coming up. The precise value of this probability is a characteristic of each particular radioactive species. The higher the probability, the more rapidly the nucleus may be expected to disintegrate. But a given nucleus need not do at any particular time what is expected of it.

The notion of probability (or chance) has meaning only when applied to a large number of cases. To say that a given nucleus has one chance in a hundred of decaying in the next second means that out of some large number (say 100 million) of such radioactive nuclei, one per cent (one million) will decay in the next second. But it is absolutely impossible to say beforehand which nuclei will be the ones to decay. A particular nucleus may decay immediately or only after some very long time. The collection as a whole, however, will always do the expected thing. (This is the principle on which insurance companies operate.)

The situation is best described in terms of a time span which is called the half-life of the radioactive species. The half-life is defined as the amount of time which is required for one half of a large number of identical radioactive nuclei to disintegrate. It makes no difference what this large number is, provided only that it is large enough.

If the number is not large enough, fluctuations will occur, and instead of 50 per cent of the nuclei decaying during the period of a half-life, it may be 40 per cent or 60 per cent. As a matter of fact the 40 per cent to 60 per cent limits correspond to a sample size of about 100 nuclei. For 10,000 nuclei, the limits will be 49 per cent to 51 per cent. The number of radioactive nuclei with which we customarily deal, is about 10^{23} (100,000,000,000 ,000,000,000,000). This is the number, for example, of radioactive nuclei in about an ounce of radium. For such a large number of nuclei the deviation from 50-per-cent decay during a half-life will be utterly negligible. Thus we live in a universe which, on a macroscopic scale, appears ordered and subject to exact laws; while underlying these laws, on a microscopic scale, nature plays out a game of chance, full of randomness and uncertainty in the individual case.

We may draw a graph showing how N, the number of the

remaining radioactive nuclei, varies with the time t. The graph shows that: in the first half-life T, half of the original number N_o of radioactive nuclei decay. In the second half-

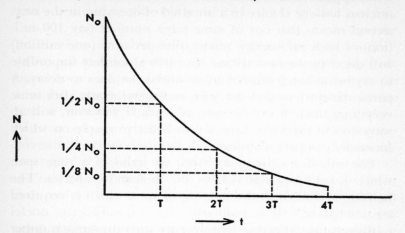

life, half of those remaining decay, and so on. After the time T, one half of the original radioactive nuclei still remain; after $2T$, one quarter remain; and so forth.

Different radioactive species have different half-lives. Many are only a small fraction of a second; some are billions of years. N^{16} decays to O^{16} (plus an electron and a neutrino) with a half-life of about eight seconds. A free neutron decays into a proton, an electron, and a neutrino with a half-life of 13 minutes. Strontium with weight 90 (Sr^{90}) undergoes a beta decay with a half-life of 28 years. (This is an isotope that is not found anywhere in nature, but is made in fairly large quantities in the fission process.) Potassium with weight 40 (K^{40}), which is present in the amount of 0.01 per cent in ordinary potassium, has a half-life of one billion years. It has presumably been left over from the time when the primordial elements were formed. Half-lives for gamma decay are extremely short by comparison to those for beta decay. They usually amount to a small fraction of a second.

Radioactivity is characterized by the kind of particle emitted from the nucleus (our examples, so far, have been of beta and gamma particles), by the energy possessed by this particle, and by the half-life in which the radioactive decay takes place.

The biological hazard from radioactivity depends on all three of these characteristics. No matter whether the radioactive nuclei are produced in an atomic explosion or in an atomic reactor, some time will in general elapse before a human population can become exposed. If this time is long compared to the half-life of the radioactive species, most of the nuclei will have disintegrated, and the hazard will thereby be reduced. If, on the other hand, the half-life is long compared to this time, as well as to the life-span of a human being, the rate at which disintegrations occur will be low, and again the hazard will be reduced.

In short the dangerous half-lives are the intermediate ones, not too long, not too short. Sr^{90} is an example.

CHAPTER V

Breakup of the Nucleus

THE POSITIVE electric charges within an atomic nucleus repel one another. In the most heavily charged nuclei this repulsion becomes so great that the nucleus can break into two parts, simultaneously releasing a considerable amount of energy. In the case of *spontaneous nuclear fission* the two parts are more or less equal in size. In the process of *alpha decay* one of the parts (the alpha particle) is much smaller than the other.

An alpha particle consists of two neutrons and two protons and is identical with the nucleus of the helium atom. (The symbol for this nucleus is He^4.) Since two neutrons and two protons can simultaneously occupy the lowest energy state, the alpha particle is an especially stable nuclear unit. As a result, from time to time in heavy nuclei, two neutrons and two protons will coalesce into an alpha particle, which may then attempt to escape.

In attempting to escape from the nucleus, however, an alpha particle encounters considerable resistance because of the short-range nuclear attraction of the other neutrons and protons. This resistance which an alpha particle experiences in trying to leave the nucleus is usually referred to as an "energy barrier." If the alpha particle could acquire a little additional energy, it would be able to overcome the barrier and get away from the nuclear attraction. Once outside the nucleus, just beyond the reach of the nuclear attraction, the alpha particle would be accelerated violently outward by the large electrical repulsion between its two protons and the other protons in the residual nucleus.

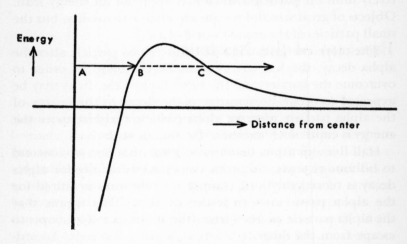

How an alpha particle escapes from the nucleus. From A to B it goes "uphill," losing speed. At B its speed is zero and it almost always turns around. With a small probability it may sneak through the energy barrier B to C. Beyond C, it is repelled and emerges with increasing speed.

The alpha particle needs some extra energy to escape. According to the laws of older physics there is no possibility for it to obtain this extra energy and therefore escape is impossible. But the more newly discovered laws governing the motion of neutrons and protons (the laws of quantum mechanics) are not so stringent; they permit the alpha particle to use "borrowed" energy to overcome the energy barrier. Of course the alpha particle must always repay the loan—which it can easily do out of the large fund of electric energy that is released when it gets out of the repulsive range of the residual nucleus. There is no interest on the loan.

Such energy loans are not automatically granted in nature. There are two factors which make the loan improbable: if the amount is big or if the term is long. These restrictions effectively limit the particles which may apply for an energy loan. Objects of great size and weight are unable to qualify, but the small particles of the atomic world often do.

The more energy carried off by the alpha particle after the alpha decay, the less energy must be borrowed in order to overcome the barrier, and the more rapidly the decay may be expected to occur. So sensitive is the decay to the energy of the alpha particle, that an alpha particle carrying twice the energy is emitted a hundred trillion times faster.

Half-lives for alpha decay vary from a fraction of a second to billions of years. But even the shortest half-life for alpha decay is remarkably long compared to the time required for the alpha particle to cross the nucleus. This means that the alpha particle makes a tremendous number of attempts to escape from the nucleus before it actually succeeds. According to the older classical theory the alpha process should never occur, and in fact it occurs with a very small probability.

A single alpha decay is not usually a sufficient process to bring about stability of the daughter nucleus. A whole chain of radioactive decays is usually required before stability is achieved. Most nuclei which emit alpha particles belong to one of these radioactive decay chains.

The heavy nuclei for which alpha decay occurs all contain a large excess of neutrons. Since the alpha particle carries off exactly two neutrons and two protons, the ratio of the number of neutrons to the number of protons is increased in the daughter nucleus. This has an unstabilizing influence. (Actually, in lighter nuclei stability requires that the ratio of neutrons to protons be closer to unity.) The daughter nucleus is thus apt to be beta-active, converting a neutron into a proton (plus an electron and a neutrino) in order to decrease its ratio of neutrons to protons. In this way a chain of radioactive decays may occur, more or less alternating between alpha and beta emissions, with gamma rays being occasionally emitted also.

There are four radioactive chains. One of them starts with the abundant isotope of uranium, U^{238}. This isotope undergoes a few alpha decays and a couple of beta decays to become radium, which has a charge of 88 and a weight of 226. All the radium in the world is produced in this manner as a daughter product in the fifth decay of the chain. After a number of further decays, stable lead (weight 206) is produced and the chain terminates.

The other chains are similar to the U^{238} chain, though not quite as long. One chain starts with the rare isotope of uranium, U^{235}; another starts with the isotope of thorium that weighs 232. Both of these terminate in stable isotopes of lead. In all cases the first decay of the chain has a very long half-life. The half-life of U^{238} is 4.5 billion years; of U^{235}, 710 million years; and of thorium, 14 billion years.

The fourth radioactive chain has been made in the laboratory but is not found in nature because its first isotope, neptunium with weight 237, has too short a half-life. It decays in two million years and all the other members of the chain live for even shorter periods. Thus the neptunium chain decayed long ago, whereas the three other chains have survived from the time when the elements were made.

It is interesting to notice that the lesser abundance of U^{235}, as compared with U^{238}, is connected with its shorter half-life. Assuming that comparable amounts of both isotopes were present at the beginning of the universe (and there is good reason to believe that this was the case), one would expect to find significantly less U^{235} than U^{238} after a period of a few hundred million years. After 710 million years (the half-life for U^{235}) only one half of the original number of U^{235} nuclei would still exist. But 90 per cent of the original U^{238} nuclei (half-life 4.5 billion years) would remain. From the presently observed ratio of U^{235} to U^{238} nuclei (1 to 139), it may be calculated, using the law of radioactive decay, that 6 billion years ago natural uranium consisted of equal parts of U^{235} and U^{238}. The age of the universe is hotly debated. With each passing year the universe seems to be a billion years older. Right now six billion years does not seem widely off the mark.

Natural radioactivity occurs mainly among the heavy elements, but there are a few light elements that are naturally radioactive. Of these, potassium^{40} is an especially interesting one because it can decay either by electron emission or by electron capture. The processes are:

$$\text{potassium}^{40} \rightarrow \text{calcium}^{40} + \text{electron} + \text{neutrino},$$
$$(1.1 \text{ billion years})$$

and

$$\text{potassium}^{40} + \text{electron} \rightarrow \text{argon}^{40} + \text{neutrino}.$$
$$(11 \text{ billion years})$$

Calcium^{40} and argon^{40} are both stable nuclei. The second reaction is followed immediately by a gamma ray emission from the argon^{40}. The one per cent of argon found in the earth's atmosphere comes almost entirely from the second reaction. These radioactivities are also interesting because appreciable amounts of potassium^{40} are always present in human tissue.

All nuclei at the heavy end of the periodic system are radioactive alpha emitters. Uranium, for example, has no stable isotopes; they all undergo alpha decay. But there is another mode of spontaneous decay of uranium, which is much less frequent than alpha decay but is of much greater practical importance. This is the fission process.

The fission process is just like alpha decay in that the nucleus breaks up into two fragments. The main difference between these processes is in the relative weights of the fragments. In the alpha decay of U^{238}, for instance, one fragment has a weight of four and the other 234. In the fission process the fragments tend to be more nearly equal in weight. For example, one may weigh 90 and the other 148.[1] Other weight combinations are also possible.

The explanation of spontaneous fission is in essence the same as that of alpha decay. Spontaneous fission, however, is a less probable process because the two fragments are more strongly bound to each other by the nuclear forces than they are in alpha decay. More energy must be borrowed, and it must be borrowed for a longer term in order to penetrate the energy barrier.

The relative likelihoods of spontaneous fission and alpha decay can be appreciated from the following fact. In one hour in a gram of U^{238} there occur about 45 million alpha decays but only about 25 spontaneous fissions.

Once the energy barrier has been overcome, the energy released in alpha decay or spontaneous fission is proportional to the charges on the two fragments. For alpha decay, the product of the charges is $2 \times 90 = 180$; for spontaneous fission, this product will typically be about $40 \times 52 = 2,080$. Hence one might expect the fission energy release to be 10 to 15 times greater than the alpha energy release. As a matter of fact the fission energy release is even greater than this estimate indicates, being about 30 to 50 times greater than the alpha energy release. That so large an amount of energy is released, is a very important feature of the fission process from

[1] Actually the weights rarely add up to the original 238 because, as a rule, one or more neutrons are emitted which carry off some of the original mass.

the point of view of practical utilization of atomic energy.

Being at the end of the periodic system, uranium requires a large ratio of neutrons to protons for its greatest stability. The fission fragments, however, lie in the middle of the system of elements, requiring a much smaller ratio of neutrons to protons for stability. This has two consequences.

One is that the fragments themselves may be expected to be unstable. They will undergo beta decay (electron emission) several times consecutively before a stable combination of neutrons and protons is reached. This radioactivity of the fission products constitutes a potential hazard in any practical application of fission atomic energy. In later chapters of this book we shall consider particularly the possible hazard from the fallout of radioactive fission products created in atomic explosions, and also the hazard associated with the operation and maintenance of atomic reactors.

The second consequence of the neutron excess is that neutrons may boil off from the fragments immediately after the fission process has occurred. This can happen because a lot of disorderly internal motion is generated by the fission process within the fragments, and these fragments do not have a particularly strong hold on their neutrons. The practical value of the released neutrons is something we shall discuss at length in a later chapter. For the present we mention only that these neutrons provide the mechanism whereby a chain reaction is made possible.

Spontaneous fission and alpha decay are responsible for the fact that elements with charge greater than 92 are not found in nature. There is little doubt that these elements were made in the beginning. But they have long since decayed.

An interesting case of spontaneous nuclear fission is californium[254] (charge 98), with a half-life of 55 days. This isotope is formed in large quantities in certain stellar explosions called super-novae. Once in a millennium one of a collection of a billion stars flares into incredible brilliance. For a few weeks this single star shines with the combined energy and luster of a billion ordinary stars—then it fades away gradually. Such a "new" star (nova), with the greatest power of radiation, is called a "super-nova."

We believe that many nuclear reactions take place in a super-nova. It has been observed that a few weeks after the initial outburst of light, the intensity of light is reduced almost exactly by a factor of two every 55 days for a year or so. This is precisely what would be expected if the energy generated in the star during this time were due to the spontaneous fission of californium[254]. Here we see a model of what happens to naturally radioactive elements. Of these we have retained on earth only the ones with the longest half-lives, like uranium, thorium, and potassium.

CHAPTER VI

Reactions Between Nuclei

THE ALCHEMISTS tried to transform one element into another artificially. They used heat, they used chemicals; they even used witchcraft. They failed. Their simplest method—to heat the substance in order to transform it—was really correct. The trouble was that their temperatures were too low by a factor of more than 10,000. What is needed, is a temperature of the order of tens of millions of degrees.

At such high temperatures two nuclei may occasionally approach each other in spite of the electrical repulsion between them. Sometimes they may even get close enough to each other to undergo a nuclear reaction. This, of course, happens with least difficulty if the nuclear charge is small. Hydrogen nuclei, which carry charge 1, participate in such reactions most easily.

In the interior of stars temperatures range from about 10 to 100 million degrees, and nuclear reactions do occur. The reaction responsible for the production of energy in the stars is:

$$4 \text{ H}^1 \longrightarrow \text{He}^4 + \text{energy}$$

Four protons combine to make an alpha particle with a release of energy. Actually this reaction does not take place all at once but several steps are required. That energy should be released, one expects from the fact that the alpha particle is very stable. Any process in which light nuclei combine to form a heavier nucleus with a release of energy is known as "fusion."

The particular fusion process that goes on in the stars releases its energy in many forms: as positrons, neutrinos, electromagnetic radiation, and motion of the reacting particles. The positrons also carry off the excess charge of the reaction.

The neutrinos fly through the star without interacting, carrying their energy away into outer space, probably never again to make contact with the material universe. The remainder of the fusion energy is deposited within the star's interior, which is thus kept hot enough so that the fusion reaction can keep going. The name "thermonuclear" is appropriately applied to this type of reaction.

A lot of effort and imagination is being devoted to the problem of making a controlled thermonuclear reaction. The motivation for this project comes from the fact that good thermonuclear fuels, such as deuterium (H^2), are abundant and cheap. There is enough deuterium in the oceans of the world to supply man's energy needs for many millions of years. One difficulty, of course, is to find a container for the reaction.

Even under stellar conditions the rate of fusion reactions is not very great. It takes approximately a billion years for only one per cent of the nuclei to react. Consequently even higher temperatures than those found in stars are required to produce large amounts of energy in a short time. But no known materials can withstand temperatures of more than a few thousand degrees centigrade. One idea is to keep the "burning" fuel away from material walls by means of magnetic fields.

Is there a way to make nuclei react without the extreme temperatures needed in the thermonuclear reactions? What

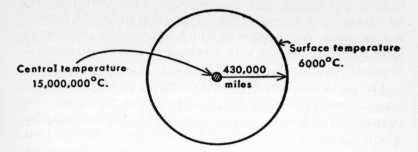

Central temperature
15,000,000°C.

430,000
miles

Surface temperature
6000°C.

Interior of the sun. The thermonuclear reactions take place mainly in the very hot, very dense central region (shaded). This region is about 20,000 miles in radius and has a density approximately 80 times the density of water.

one is really trying to do is bring two nuclear particles into intimate enough contact so that the nuclear forces can act between them. There is no reason why one should not use a *cold* target material, which is bombarded from the outside by energetic nuclear projectiles, for example protons or alpha particles. The projectiles, if they are energetic enough, can overcome the electrical repulsion of the target nuclei, and they actually can penetrate. The resulting "compound" nuclei would either be unstable and disintegrate instantaneously, or else be almost stable (i.e., radioactive) and disintegrate after some period of time. In either case nuclei of new elements would probably be formed in the reaction. This procedure sounds simple, but it has its difficulties.

The main difficulty is that the nucleus is a very tiny target. Its area is about 100 million times smaller than the area of the atom as a whole. If a piece of matter is bombarded by an energetic particle, chance alone will determine whether the particle is directed toward a nucleus. To be sure, if the particle misses the nucleus of one atom, it still has the opportunity of hitting the nuclei of other atoms which may lie in its path. It does not have many such opportunities, however, because, be-ing charged, it constantly interacts with the atomic electrons, which gradually absorb energy causing the particle to slow down.

As the particle slows down, its chance of hitting a nucleus decreases, even if it is heading directly toward one, because of the repulsion between its charge and that of the nucleus. Un-less the particle has sufficient speed, it cannot overcome this repulsion.

Charged particles may be given the required speeds by ac-celerating them through large electric fields. If a unit charge is accelerated through a potential difference of one volt, it acquires an energy of one *electron-volt*. The energies re-quired for nuclear bombardment are of the order of several million electron-volts, which can be provided by atom-smash-ing machines such as the cyclotron.

Even at such high energies very few of the nuclear projec-tiles actually find their way to a target nucleus. Most of them are slowed down by the electrons, wasting their energy in heating up the target material. Perhaps one particle out of a million will be lucky enough to induce a nuclear reaction.

If the purpose of the nuclear accelerating machines were to produce cheap energy, they would not be of much value. A nuclear reaction may typically release five to 20 million elec-tron-volts of energy. But to obtain this reaction, a million particles had to be accelerated to energies of several million electron-volts. The recoverable and useable energy will be only a minute fraction of the total invested.

On the other hand, as a tool for scientific discovery, the atom-smashers have been of great importance. That one event in a million has given us much of our knowledge of nuclear physics.

The achievement of nuclear reactions by particle bombard-ment did not actually wait on the invention of man-made ac-celerating machines. Energetic alpha particles are available from the radioactive decay of heavy elements. In 1919 Ernest Rutherford used such radioactive elements as a source of alpha particles. The alpha particles were made to bombard ordinary nitrogen, causing the reaction:

$$He^4 \quad + \quad N^{14} \longrightarrow \quad O^{17} \quad + \quad proton$$
$$\begin{pmatrix} 2 \text{ protons} \\ 2 \text{ neutrons} \end{pmatrix} \quad \begin{pmatrix} 7 \text{ protons} \\ 7 \text{ neutrons} \end{pmatrix} \quad \begin{pmatrix} 8 \text{ protons} \\ 9 \text{ neutrons} \end{pmatrix}$$

That is, an alpha particle plus a nitrogen^{14} nucleus react to produce a nucleus of (stable) oxygen^{17} plus a proton. Oxygen^{17} is a nucleus with 8 protons and 9 neutrons. The ordinary abundant form of oxygen has 8 protons and 8 neutrons. Natural oxygen contains a small amount of oxygen^{17}.

Later, in 1934, Irene Curie Joliot (the daughter of the discoverer of radium, Madame Curie) and her husband, Frederic Joliot, used naturally available alpha particles to make artificial radioactive nuclei for the first time. The reaction was:

$$He^4 + aluminum^{27} \longrightarrow phosphorus^{30} + neutron$$
$$\begin{pmatrix} 2 \text{ protons} \\ 2 \text{ neutrons} \end{pmatrix} \quad \begin{pmatrix} 13 \text{ protons} \\ 14 \text{ neutrons} \end{pmatrix} \quad \begin{pmatrix} 15 \text{ protons} \\ 15 \text{ neutrons} \end{pmatrix}$$

Phosphorus^{30} is an unstable nucleus and emits a beta ray (a positron) to become silicon^{30} (which is stable). The half-life for this decay is about 2.5 minutes. The Joliots' reaction was the first instance in which man had produced radioactivity and known it. Actually cyclotrons had been producing radioactivity in good abundance for the preceding two years—but physicists had been unaware of this fact.

It is amusing that nature has also provided us with an atom-smashing machine and indeed one that produces far greater energies than any apparatus yet devised by man. This machine operates on the principle of fluctuating, turbulent magnetic fields in interstellar space. Cosmic particles— mainly protons, but also some alpha particles and even heavier nuclei—are accelerated by these changing magnetic fields and hurled occasionally into the earth's atmosphere. The energies of these cosmic particles are enormous, ranging from billions of electron-volts to values a million times higher.

When a cosmic particle gets inside the earth's atmosphere, it does not go far before colliding with a nucleus of nitrogen or oxygen. Out of this nuclear event emerge all the fundamental particles mentioned so far, and some others known as mesons. Mesons are particles which may be charged or neutral, and which have a weight a few hundred times that of the electron. Some of these particles are believed to be connected with the forces that hold the nucleus together.

The nuclear debris from the collision will itself be very energetic and will further disrupt other nitrogen and oxygen nuclei. There soon develops a cascade of electrons, positrons, mesons, neutrons, protons, and electromagnetic radiation moving toward the surface of the earth.

About once a second every square inch of the earth's atmosphere receives such an energetic particle from outer space. The cascade that results carries penetrating radiations to the surface of the earth. All living organisms are constantly subjected to this radiation background. It is an important fact that the intensity of this radiation is reduced in its passage through the air, and inhabitants of Denver or Lima receive more cosmic radiation than the inhabitants of Los Angeles or New York.

Some neutrons made by collisions of the primary cosmic particles in the atmosphere may collide with nuclei of nitrogen. When this happens, the following reaction occurs:

$$\text{nitrogen}^{14} + \text{neutron} \longrightarrow \text{carbon}^{14} + \text{proton}$$

$$\begin{pmatrix} 7 \text{ protons} \\ 7 \text{ neutrons} \end{pmatrix} \qquad \begin{pmatrix} 6 \text{ protons} \\ 8 \text{ neutrons} \end{pmatrix}$$

Carbon^{14} is a radioactive electron emitter with a half-life of 5,600 years. This half-life is long enough so that much of the carbon^{14} in the world today was probably made ten to twenty thousand years ago. Willard Libby studied this process in a careful and quantitative way, traced the history of the radioactive carbon from the atmosphere into living beings, and, by measuring the carbon[14] content in historical remains, opened up a whole new branch of archeology.

Living organisms breathe in carbon (in the form of carbon dioxide) from the air. Most of this carbon is ordinary stable carbon[12]; a tiny fraction is radioactive carbon[14]. The organism is unable to distinguish between the two isotopes, and takes in carbon[14] in the same ratio to carbon[12] as exists in the atmosphere. This ratio persists throughout the organism's lifetime, but when the organism dies and no more carbon is assimilated, the ratio begins to decrease as the carbon[14] nuclei gradually disintegrate. By observing the ratio of carbon[14] to carbon[12] in fossil remains and other archeological objects, the date at which death occurred can be calculated. In this way the age of ancient Egyptian mummies has been found, and it has been shown that some sequoia wood is more than 1,500 years old. By measuring the carbon[14] in trees that were killed by the last advance of glaciation, and looking into other remains of life from the last ice age, it has been possible to show that this last ice age occurred only 10,000 years ago—instead of 20,000 years, as had been previously believed. Carbon[14]-dating has therefore thoroughly revised our ideas about the rapidity with which the empires known to history have emerged from the most primitive conditions. A crucial part of the argument is that isotopes of the same element are chemically indistinguishable.

An alternative reaction which may occur when neutrons strike nitrogen, is

$$N^{14} + \text{neutron} \longrightarrow \text{carbon}^{12} + H^3$$

$$\begin{pmatrix} 7 \text{ protons} \\ 7 \text{ neutrons} \end{pmatrix} \qquad \begin{pmatrix} 6 \text{ protons} \\ 6 \text{ neutrons} \end{pmatrix} \begin{pmatrix} 1 \text{ proton} \\ 2 \text{ neutrons} \end{pmatrix}$$

H^3; triton, is also radioactive, undergoing a beta decay to become He^3 (2 protons and 1 neutron) with a half-life of 12.25 years. Tritons too can be used for dating old objects— for example, old wine. The water in the wine cannot be replenished with cosmic-ray tritons after the wine has been bottled. Thus fifty per cent of the tritons disappear every 12.25 years.

We have here two examples of nuclear reactions induced by neutron bombardment. Recalling the disadvantages of charged particles as nuclear projectiles for alchemists, it must surely seem that neutrons would be ideal for this purpose. Being chargeless, they are neither electrically repelled by the nuclei nor constantly slowed down by energy-losing collisions with the electrons. The fate of almost every neutron moving in a large piece of matter is eventual collision with a nucleus.[1] Neutrons are ideal nuclear projectiles, except for one thing: they are hard to get.

Protons and alpha particles are found abundantly in nature as the nuclei of hydrogen and helium atoms. Neutrons, however, are not found in nature, and in the past have been made in nuclear reactions that were themselves initiated by charged particles. For example,

$$He^4 \quad + \quad beryllium^9 \longrightarrow \quad C^{12} \quad + \quad neutron$$
$$\begin{pmatrix} 2 \text{ protons} \\ 2 \text{ neutrons} \end{pmatrix} \begin{pmatrix} 4 \text{ protons} \\ 5 \text{ neutrons} \end{pmatrix} \begin{pmatrix} 6 \text{ protons} \\ 6 \text{ neutrons} \end{pmatrix}$$

But now we encounter again the difficulty associated with charged particles. Only one alpha particle in a million undergoes a nuclear reaction to produce a neutron. The neutron, of course, makes a nuclear reaction every time. Over-all, then, we obtain two nuclear reactions per million nuclear projectiles, instead of one per million. With such methods we are not so much better off than the old alchemists. A cheap and plentiful source of neutrons would, however, put

---

[1] Only a very few unlucky ones are overtaken by beta decay first.

the alchemist in business. In this way one could make rare elements and radioactive isotopes, and what is more important, he would be able to utilize concentrated nuclear energy.

CHAPTER VII

Fission and the Chain Reaction

NEUTRONS ARE ideal projectiles for nuclear bombardment because they carry no charge, can approach nuclei easily, and interact with them strongly. These neutral particles, discovered by James Chadwick in 1932, were used soon afterward by Enrico Fermi and his collaborators to bombard most of the elements of the periodic table. Very often in these experiments a nucleus would capture a neutron and become unstable with too much weight for its charge. Stability would then be restored by a beta decay, leaving the nucleus with one more unit of charge than it had to begin with. In 1934 Fermi tried this experiment with uranium, charge 92, the most highly charged element known at that time. He hoped to make a transuranic element with charge 93.

Throughout the experiments the uranium was observed with radioactive counters and found to become far more radioactive than uranium ordinarily is in its natural state. There was no way to account for all this radioactivity except to assume that new elements had been formed in the process of neutron bombardment. A chemical analysis revealed no elements with charges between 86 and 91. From this evidence Fermi concluded that no elements of charge less than 92 had been made and therefore the radioactivity must be due to charges greater than 92. He concluded that transuranic elements had been made in the laboratory.

Neither Fermi nor anyone else, however, was happy with this conclusion. There was far too great a variety of radioactivity for comfort. It had to be assumed that not only was the element with charge 93 being made, but also elements with charges 94, 95, and many more. This was very hard to understand. Ida Noddack,[1] a chemist, published a paper proposing an alternative explanation of the experiment: that a nucleus of uranium, when it captures a neutron, might break up into two fragments that could have any of various weights and charges. In other words, she suggested that Fermi had produced nuclear fission.

Fermi, however, believed that the fission process was an impossibility. He had a convincing proof, based on the measured values of the weights of nuclei and the formula of Einstein, $E = mc^2$. From this formula Fermi calculated the energy liberated when uranium breaks into two pieces; then he took into account the energy of electric repulsion between the pieces and found that the energy barrier was so large that the fission process could not take place. This proof was absolutely correct. The only trouble was that the measured values of the weights of nuclei happened to be inaccurate at that time!

But for this accident, fission would have been discovered in 1934 instead of 1938. If it had been, Nazi Germany might easily have been the first country to make the atomic bomb. At that time some German scientists were active in the field of military applications. The American physicists had not yet turned much attention to the subject.

[1] She and her husband were the discoverers of two elements, rhenium and masurium. One of these exists.

An important feature of Fermi's experiment is the large amount and variety of radioactivity that he found. The reason for this variety, as we now know, is that the fission process does not take place in a unique manner. The two primary fission fragments are very rarely of equal weight and charge. On the average the lighter fragment weighs about 90, and the heavier one about 140. Sometimes the lighter fragment will weigh as little as 75, and the heavier one as much as 160. As the weight varies, of course, so also does the charge. The charge of the lighter fragment averages 38, which is strontium, and the heavier one 54, which is xenon. All in all there are more than a hundred different species of nuclei represented among the primary fission fragments.

Practically all of these nuclei are radioactive and undergo three or four disintegrations before reaching stability. Overall therefore, several hundred distinct radioactive species are created by the fission process in uranium. Elements with charges 43 and 61 (which are not found in nature) have been identified as fission products in fairly appreciable quantities. Most of the fission products are short-lived electron and gamma emitters that can contribute only to the local and immediate radioactive hazard. Two of the long-lived products are abundant and important. These are cesium[137] and strontium[90].

Cesium[137] has a half-life of 30 years and emits a gamma ray with an energy of 0.6 million electron-volts. Strontium[90] has a half-life of 28 years and emits an electron with an average energy of 0.22 million electron-volts. The daughter nucleus in this process is yttrium[90], which emits another electron with an average energy of one million electron-volts. The half-life of yttrium[90] is 64 hours. In effect, therefore, strontium[90] emits two electrons, each with an average energy of 0.6 million electron-volts. For the long-term radioactive hazard, particularly the world-wide fallout associated with atomic explosions, the two isotopes cesium[137] and strontium[90] are the most significant. Strontium[90] is the more dangerous to living organisms because it is deposited in the bones and retained in the body for long periods.

Besides radioactivity there is another feature of the fission process which is so conspicuous that it may seem hard to understand how Fermi failed to notice it—namely the large amount of energy released. The fission of a single nucleus of uranium releases an energy of 200 million electron-volts as contrasted with ordinary radioactive decay energies of 5 to 10 million electron-volts. (The energy released from the burning of one atom of coal is only 4 electron-volts.)

Of the 200 million electron-volts released in fission, about 10 million go into gamma rays and neutrons created in the fission process itself. This energy contributes to the immediate and local radiation danger. Another 24 million electron-volts go into radioactivity of the fission products, and of this, about half go into neutrinos, which are neither dangerous nor useful; the other half is carried by electrons and gives rise to the delayed radioactive hazard. But the bulk of the energy, over 160 million electron-volts, goes into kinetic energy of the two primary fission fragments. Of this amount, 100 million, on the average, go to the lighter fragment.

One hundred million electron-volt fission fragments should certainly have been noticed by Fermi's radioactive counters —if they had been able to reach the counters. The fragments were not able to reach the counters, however. The reason is that Fermi was a careful worker. He knew that his sample of uranium would emit some radioactive particles even before neutron bombardment. This natural radioactivity he did not want to get mixed up with the radioactivity that would be produced in the experiment. So he put an absorbing foil between the uranium sample and the radioactive counters. The fission fragments could not get through the foil.

It is amusing that shortly afterward another noted physicist repeated Fermi's experiment, but this time without the foil. He reported that he was unable to get any significant results because his counter, for reasons unknown, started to spark.

Thus fission remained a secret. But in England Leo Szilard obtained patent papers on the nuclear chain reaction. He pointed out that in some nuclear reactions free neutrons might be released. These neutrons might then succeed in producing further reactions which would produce more neutrons. Provided that at least one neutron made in each reaction were able to induce a reaction in another nucleus, a chain reaction would take place.

The main problem, of course, was to avoid excessive neutron losses. There are two ways in which the losses mainly occur. One is by wasteful, nonreproductive capture in the nuclei; the other, by neutron leakage from the material surface. This second loss, Szilard showed, could be minimized by using a sufficiently large amount of chain-reacting material.

The point is that a neutron born in a nuclear reaction must travel on the average a certain distance before it can produce another reaction. If the size of the chain-reacting material is much less than this distance, practically all of the neutrons produced will be able to escape through the material surface, and no chain reaction will be possible. If the size of the material is large compared to this distance, the leakage loss becomes negligible, and the possibility of a chain reaction depends entirely on the magnitude of the first kind of loss, the wasteful captures in nuclei. If this loss is not too great, and a chain reaction is possible, there will be a *critical* size of the material at which on the average exactly one neutron per reaction will be able to induce another reaction. A just critical chain reaction of this kind is what is needed for an atomic reactor.

If the size of the material is greater than the critical size, on the average more than one neutron per reaction will cause another reaction and the chain reaction will run away. If, for example, two neutrons can cause another reaction, there will be two neutrons after the first generation, four after the second, eight after the third, and so forth. This is the principle of the atomic bomb.

After about 80 generations, an appreciable fraction of all the nuclei in the material will have undergone a nuclear transformation and so much energy will have been released that the material will not stay together even for the short time needed to produce the next generation. The whole material begins to fly apart, the system becomes sub-critical, and the chain reaction stops. The entire process lasts only a fraction of a microsecond.

Thus even before fission was discovered, Szilard laid the basis for constructing the atomic bomb and the nuclear chain reactor. As materials in which a chain reaction might conceivably be made to occur he named thorium, uranium and beryllium. On beryllium he was wrong because the mass of this atom was incorrectly known. On thorium, his guess was good. On uranium, he hit the bull's eye.

Finally in December 1938 the secret broke. Hahn and Strassmann in Germany made a chemical analysis of a uranium target that had been exposed to neutrons. They were far more thorough than previous investigators had been, and they found barium, charge 56, which had not been present in the target material before the experiment. The only possible explanation was the fission process. Within a few weeks the violent kicks caused by the fission products in counters were found, and in the following days this experiment was repeated around the world.

There was no doubt that neutrons could induce fission in uranium nuclei. A few more weeks, and it was ascertained that the fission process released neutrons which might lead to more fissions.

The chain reaction, however, was still far from a reality. Niels Bohr and John Wheeler proved that a neutron could not cause fission in U^{238} unless its energy were greater than about one million electron-volts. When the neutrons are first made in the fission process, many of them do have energies greater than one million electron-volts. But before they can cause a fission, they usually make a few nonfission collisions with uranium nuclei, giving part of their energy to the nuclei and escaping with the remainder. The nuclei are then left with too little energy to undergo fission and the neutrons with too little energy to cause fissions in their next encounters. Thus too few neutrons reproduce themselves and no chain is possible.

Bohr and Wheeler suggested, however, that the rare isotope of uranium, U^{235}, can undergo fission when any neutron, even a slow neutron, hits it. Thus a chain reaction is possible in U^{235}. This was confirmed experimentally shortly afterwards by John Dunning and Alfred Drier and their coworkers at Columbia University.

Why the isotopes 235 and 238 behave so differently, is not difficult to understand. The 235 is more explosive and more prone to undergo fission than 238 because it is smaller and therefore its protons repel each other more strongly. More important still, when a neutron is captured by 235, it acquires a greater kinetic energy by virtue of the short-range nuclear attraction than a neutron acquires when it is captured by 238. This happens for the simple reason that nuclei tend to be more stable when they have an even number of neutrons (or protons) than when they have an odd number. U^{235}, having an odd number of neutrons, is more eager to receive an additional neutron than 238, which already has an even number of neutrons. Consequently, the capture of a slow neutron by 235 almost always eventuates in the fission process; while in 238, the excess energy, introduced by the neutron, is merely ejected from the nucleus in the form of a gamma ray, and U^{238} becomes U^{239}.

A chain reaction is possible in U^{235}, but it is necessary to separate this rare isotope from the abundant U^{238}. The separation process is anything but simple since isotopes of the same element are chemically indistinguishable. Even the weight difference in this case, is little more than one per cent. Bohr rejected the idea of a large-scale separation with the remark: "You would have to turn the whole country into a factory." Of course it is now a matter of history that the job was actually done under the Manhattan project during World War II. During the war Bohr (alias Nicholas Baker) again visited the United States and was shown the separation plants. He said: "You see I was right. You *did* turn the country into a factory."

Natural uranium contains U^{235} in the ratio of 1 part to 139 of U^{238}. It was hoped at first that this concentration would be sufficient to make a chain reaction, and that the expensive enrichment processes could be avoided. This seemed possible because at energies of a fraction of an electron-volt the neutrons are much more easily caught by U^{235} than by U^{238}, which compensates for the low concentration. Actually neutrons are slowed down until their energy is as low as the energy of all other particles participating in the general agitation caused by the temperature. This energy is low enough for the purpose.

However, the neutrons are made in the fission process with an energy of about a million electron-volts. Before they slow down sufficiently, they must pass through a stage in which their energy is about 7 electron-volts. In the neighborhood of this energy, it happens that the U^{238} has an extremely high probability for capturing a neutron and changing into U^{239}. Near some other energies, similar though smaller absorption hurdles must be passed. Therefore natural uranium by itself cannot be used to make a chain reaction. In 1940, Fermi and Szilard, working now in the United States, found a way around this difficulty.

Their trick was to mix the natural uranium with a material whose nuclei are so lightweight that they suffer a big recoil when struck by a neutron and thus absorb a large fraction of the neutron energy. The neutron is thus *moderated* down to a low energy, rapidly and in big energy jumps, so that either it does not spend much time at the unfavorable energies where it can be caught by U^{238} or else it misses these energies altogether. By imbedding the uranium in lumps in the moderating material instead of making a homogeneous mixture of the two, the absorption can be circumvented even better.

For the purpose of making a *controlled* chain reaction, one may use the method of enrichment, or the method of moderation, or both. But to produce a *violent* chain reaction, an atomic bomb, only the enrichment method will work. The reason is that all the energy of the bomb must be generated in a time that is as short as the time it takes the bomb to fly apart, which is a fraction of a microsecond. If natural uranium were used, the reaction would be slow and sluggish and would be extinguished before a substantial fraction of the nuclei could have reacted.

It is interesting to consider that chain-reacting substances could have been obtained easily six billion years ago, before the U^{235} had time to decay and become a rare isotope. (The U^{235} was then about as abundant as U^{238}.) A chemical separation would still have been necessary and so we do not need to imagine that chain-reacting mixtures accumulated spontaneously on the young earth.

On the other hand, six billion years from now U^{235} will have become so rare that it will be impossible to get a reactor going by moderation. At the same time the isotope separation will have become most expensive since the isotope to be separated will be present in an abundance of less than 100 parts in a million. For those who like to worry about the distant future we should hasten to add that other methods of obtaining atomic energy will remain possible. And in any case there is good reason to believe that some stellar explosions produce fresh supplies of U^{235} which space merchants could undoubtedly make available.

As to our present terrestrial supplies: uranium, like other heavy elements, is quite rare. But the earth is divided into layers of which the topmost 10 miles, forming something of a slag or scum, contain quite a few rare compounds. In particular almost all of the uranium in our planet is conveniently collected right under our feet, for us to use as we see fit.

CHAPTER VIII

Action of Radiation on Matter

WHEN AN energetic particle moves through matter (living or nonliving), what happens is a question of chemistry. Chemistry is the subject that deals with the arrangement and rearrangement of electrons in atoms and molecules. A chemical rearrangement generally requires an energy in the neighborhood of a few electron-volts. (As we have seen, an electron-volt is the energy released when an electron moves through a potential of one volt, i.e., a little less than one per cent of the driving force in a standard electric outlet.) An energetic particle, such as might be emitted in a radioactive decay, typically has an energy of a few million electron-volts. Thus a single such particle has the potentiality of about a million chemical rearrangements.

Energetic particles may be charged or neutral, light or heavy, or electromagnetic in nature. Because of this diversity one might think there would be no common grounds for comparing the action on matter of different particles. Each particle might conceivably make its own inimitable variety of chemical rearrangements. Actually this is not the case.

Unlike some chemical poisons, which seek out specific molecules in our body, the energetic particles strike at whatever atoms or molecules happen to get in their way. They act, in this sense, like a sledge hammer. Their effects can be measured directly from the strength (or energy) of the blow. Which particle delivers the blow is of little consequence provided the same amount of energy is delivered and provided the same tissues are affected (in the case of living matter). After the blow, however, some specific chemical effects may occur. When water or some other molecule in the body is broken up by radiation, the fragments produced may themselves be chemical poisons and attack the biologically important large molecules in a secondary way. In fact, it seems probable that a considerable part of the radiation damage caused in living systems, both healthwise and genetically, occurs in this manner.

Although the energetic particles are all similar in their ultimate action on matter, namely in producing wholesale destruction of atoms and molecules, they differ somewhat in the way in which they bring about this destruction. Charged particles act in one way, gamma rays in another, and neutrons in still another. It is simplest to begin our discussion with the charged particles.

The most important charged particles are those connected with the natural background of radioactivity and cosmic rays, and the fission process. These include alpha rays, beta rays, mesons, and fission fragments. For review, a table of the weights and charges of these particles, as well as a few others, is shown. As usual, we have used the weight and charge of the proton as units.

Particle	Weight	Charge
proton	1	1
alpha	4	2
electron ⎫ beta rays	1/1840	−1
positron ⎭	1/1840	1
deuteron	2	1
triton	3	1
meson	1/8	1, −1
average light fission fragment	97	20
average heavy fission fragment	138	22

If the fission fragments were completely stripped of their orbital electrons, they would have charges even greater than the values indicated in the table. The reader will recall that the average charge of the nucleus of the light fission fragment is 38, and of the heavy, 54. But such highly positively charged particles exert an enormous attraction on electrons. Some of these remain attached even during the fission process itself. As the fission products lose their speed during passage through matter, they pick up more electrons and gradually lose their charge.

When any of these energetic charged particles moves through matter, it interacts with electrons in the atoms. As a result of this interaction, the electrons may be dislodged from their usual states of motion. If the interaction is gentle —either because the charged particle passes the atom at a considerable distance or else because the particle is moving so rapidly that the interaction lasts for only a short time— the electron may be left undisturbed. If the interaction is more violent, however, the electron may be excited to a more energetic state of motion while still remaining in the same atom or molecule; or it may actually be ejected, ending up at some other atomic site. In this latter event the original atom is left with a residual positive charge and is said to be *ionized*. At the same time the displaced electron is apt to unite with whatever atom or molecule happens to be nearby, creating in this way a negative ion. The whole process may be described as forming an ion pair. In the wake of the charged particle one finds, therefore, ionized and excited atoms and molecules. A rearrangement of atoms will now ensue which leads to new chemical compounds. The important thing for us is, however, that these chemical changes do not depend very much on the type of particle which produced the ionization; the proportion between ionization, excitation, and eventual chemical reaction remains more or less the same. Roughly speaking, the more ion pairs that are formed in living cells, the greater is the extent of biological damage.

To make an ion pair requires the expenditure of a certain amount of energy. It might seem as though this amount should depend crucially on the weight, charge, and energy of the particle, and also on the medium through which the particle is moving. This is not so. There is some dependence, of course, but only slight. Any charged particle, irrespective of its energy, moving in any medium—air, water, soil, or living tissue—creates ion pairs at the rate of about one per 32 electron-volts. A one-million-electron-volt particle produces about 30,000 ion pairs before losing all of its energy. (When it does lose its energy, if it is a positively charged particle, it will pick up enough electrons to become neutral. An alpha particle, for example, will become an ordinary helium atom; a proton will become an atom of hydrogen.)

We have said that two charged particles having the same energy, produce the same total number of ionizations. There is an important respect, however, in which charged particles of the same energy may differ. That is, in the density of ionization along their paths. In particular, the more slowly the particle is moving and the greater its charge, the more ionization and damage it will produce in a given distance. At the same time it will lose energy at a greater rate. If we compare two charged particles of the same energy plowing into matter, the one which leaves the deeper furrow will be stopped more quickly.

For a greater charge it is easy to understand that the electrical interaction is increased and hence each atomic electron is more strongly disturbed. If, on the other hand, the particle moves more slowly (which is usually the case if it is heavy) it spends a longer time in the neighborhood of the atomic electrons. The electrical interaction thus has a longer duration and is more effective in ejecting an electron. For this same reason the density of ionization along the path of a particular charged particle should tend to become greater and greater as the particle slows down. Actually this tendency is opposed in the case of a fission fragment by the increased likelihood of the particle's picking up electrons and reducing its charge. As a result, the ionization density for these fragments is rather uniform. If a heavily charged, slow particle moves through matter it leaves so many disturbed and disrupted molecules behind that now these molecules may react with each other. Therefore heavy ionization may lead to peculiar effects. Nevertheless all ionizing particles give rise to roughly similar chemical change and destruction.

Except for the beta rays, all the charged particles are very heavy compared to the electron. Consequently, as they move through matter and interact with the atomic electrons, their paths are not perceptibly deflected from the original direction. The beta rays, on the other hand, having the same weight as the atomic electrons, are appreciably affected by their encounters and are frequently forced to change direction. Their paths are thus winding and random.

Because the beta ray does not travel in a straight line, its ability to penetrate matter must not be measured by its total path length. As a rule of thumb, the *range* of a beta particle, being the distance it travels along the line of its original direction, is about one half of its total path length. For heavier charged particles, however, no distinction need be made between range and actual distance traveled.

The most important fact about the ranges of charged particles is that they are small. An alpha particle, for instance, with a typical radioactive energy of a few million electron-volts, has a range in water (or living tissue) of a few thousandths of an inch. Such a particle could not penetrate a sheet of paper. A fission fragment, despite its great energy, is even less penetrating than the alpha particle. The proton has a somewhat greater range than the alpha particle. But the beta ray, because of its low weight, has by far the greatest range of any of the charged particles. Even it, however, goes only a fraction of an inch in solid or liquid materials.

The following table shows the ranges (in inches) of some of the charged particles in air and water as a function of energy (in millions of electron-volts):

				Range				
	Air				*Water*			
					(Same as living tissue)			
Energy	*.5*	*1*	*2*	*5*	*.5*	*1*	*2*	*5*
alpha	0.1	0.2	0.4	1.4	0.0001	0.0002	0.0004	0.0014
proton	0.3	0.9	2.8	13.4	0.0005	0.001	0.003	0.014
beta	49.	130.	300.	770.	0.063	0.16	0.38	1.0

The table shows that charged particles travel only short distances in matter. For this reason these particles are not a serious external radiation hazard. The protons and the alpha rays are usually stopped by less than a foot of air. Ordinary clothing or even the outer layer of our skin (which is composed of nonliving cells) will stop them completely.

Beta rays are stopped by less than seventy feet of air or an inch or less of solid material. (Actually most of the beta rays produced in the fission process have energies less than a million electron-volts or so, and hence their ranges are even smaller.) Radioactive contamination of beta emitters directly on one's clothes or body could cause trouble; but a good scrubbing soon after exposure will eliminate this problem. The interior of a house or building should be quite safe from any outside source of charged particles emitted by radioactive substances except possibly the most energetic beta rays. Only if the source of charged particles is inside the body so that in spite of their limited ranges the particles can find their way to sensitive tissues, is there any danger. In this case, as we shall see in a later chapter, the danger may be considerable.

Charged particles of one type stand pretty much by themselves. These are the mesons found in cosmic rays. These particles move as fast as energetic beta rays and, like the beta rays, carry unit charge. Their biological effects are therefore the same as the biological effects of beta radiation, with one important difference. The cosmic ray mesons carry much more energy and therefore have a much greater range. Whereas the beta rays are stopped in the skin, the mesons can cause damage throughout the entire body. The mesons produce the same effects as a substance which emits beta radiation uniformly in the whole body. This fact is important. It puts us in the position to compare effects of man-made radioactivity with effects of the cosmic rays to which we are constantly exposed.

Not all the energy in cosmic rays is carried by mesons. We also find showers of electrons. These are almost the same as beta rays except that they have more energy and arrive frequently in fairly sizeable numbers traveling along nearly parallel tracks. Their effects, however, are the same as the effects of the mesons.

We have been talking now about the interactions between charged particles and the atomic electrons. No mention has been made of interactions between the charged particles and nuclei. Nuclear interactions do occur sometimes, but by and large they have only a negligible influence in slowing down the charged particle. They do affect, however, beta rays.

When a beta ray collides with a highly charged nucleus, the beta particle is violently deflected. The violence of this process is due to the heavy charge of the nucleus and the small mass of the beta particle. In the sudden change of velocity which occurs, part of the electric force field which surrounds the electron breaks loose; the result is high-frequency radiation called X-rays. The importance of such electromagnetic radiation is that it can penetrate more deeply into matter. In our bodies, for typical beta-ray energies, only a small part of the beta-ray energy is converted into X-rays. But in many radioactive processes gamma rays (which are physically the same as X-rays) are produced quite abundantly.

These rays may carry as much or more energy than the beta rays.

Unlike charged particles, which constantly interact as they move through matter, gamma rays can go for long distances without having a single encounter. The actual distance depends on the energy of the gamma ray, the medium in which it moves, and pure chance. On the average, a one-million-volt gamma ray goes about six inches in water before anything at all happens to it. A four-million-volt gamma ray goes about a foot. In living matter the distances are approximately the same. Thus gamma rays from an external source can find their way deep inside the body.

Of course living matter is not injured by the mere presence of a gamma ray. There is a small probability that the gamma ray could go right through the body without a single encounter. If so, there would be no biological effect. An effect is produced only when the gamma ray interacts with the matter. There are three most important ways in which such an interaction may occur.

One way is simple *absorption* of the gamma ray by one of the atomic electrons. The gamma ray disappears in this process, and the electron acquires all of its energy. A tiny bit of this energy is used for the electron to break its bond with the atom. The remainder goes into kinetic motion of the electron. The electron is now on the loose and can cause biological damage by exciting and ionizing other atomic electrons. In fact it is now the same thing which we used to call a beta ray.

A second way in which the gamma ray may interact with matter is by *scattering*. In this case the gamma ray does not disappear but merely loses a part of its energy to the atomic electron. Again the electron is free to cause biological damage, while the gamma ray goes on to its next encounter.

The third way requires that the gamma ray be near a

nucleus and have an energy greater than a million electron-volts. (Ordinary X-rays such as are used in medical practice are not energetic enough for this process to occur.) Under these conditions the gamma ray may disappear, with the simultaneous appearance of an electron and a positron. This is an example of the creation of matter out of pure energy. In accordance with the formula $E = mc^2$, a part of the gamma-ray energy is consumed in producing particles with definite masses. This amounts to about one million electron-volts. The remainder of the gamma-ray energy goes into kinetic motion of the two particles. Again biological damage results from the subsequent ionization due to the charged particles. After the positron has expended its kinetic energy in the ionization process, it will join with an electron in a disappearing act. The energy reappears in the form of two or three gamma rays (each having less energy than the original gamma ray).

In no case is the gamma ray directly responsible for any biological damage. The damage is always made by electrons (or positrons) to which the gamma ray has transferred some or all of its energy. But this only makes gamma rays the more dangerous. They can first penetrate to the sensitive tissues of the body, and then cause ionization.

We have already mentioned that X-rays are the same as gamma rays. The latter are produced by an excited nucleus, the former in the collison of an electron (or a beta ray) with a nucleus. The man-made X-rays are obtained by first accelerating a stream of electrons and then letting them impinge on a target containing highly charged nuclei.

The usefulness of X-rays is, of course, due to their power of penetration; that is the same property which renders X-rays dangerous. One can use X-rays to find out what happens to be inside the human body. But this cannot be done without producing some disruption and rearrangement in the tissues which lie in the path of the X-rays. The damage is of the same kind as that caused by radioactivity or cosmic rays.

The effects of neutrons on matter are rather similar to the effects of gamma rays. Like gamma rays, neutrons can travel long distances in matter without interacting. On the average, a million-volt neutron goes a few inches in water before having a collision of any kind. Also like the gamma rays, the neutrons are not themselves directly responsible for any biological damage. Being neutral, they interact only with the atomic nuclei to which they are strongly attracted. By far the most important of these interactions is with the nuclei of hydrogen. There are a great number of these in living tissue in the form of protein and water molecules.

The collisions with hydrogen nuclei (i.e., protons) are important because a large fraction of the neutron energy is transferred in the process. This happens because the neutron and the proton have very nearly the same weight. If the neutron hits a heavy nucleus, it loses only a small fraction of its energy in the impact.[1] After colliding with hydrogen or a heavier nucleus, the neutron continues on to other such collisions. The nucleus, however, being charged and energetic, now causes excitation and ionization of atomic electrons. Thus, like gamma rays, energetic neutrons are exceedingly dangerous, because they can first penetrate and then cause ionization.

Neutrons are dangerous even when they are not energetic. A nonenergetic neutron may react with nuclei of living matter in a number of ways of which two are particularly probable. Either the neutron may be captured by a proton to form a deuteron, in which case the excess energy will be emitted in the form of a two-million-volt gamma ray that will cause further damage. Or the neutron may react with a nucleus of nitrogen[14] (abundantly present in living matter)

[1] A great portion of the energy might be lost if the neutron is quite fast. In this case the neutron can cause internal excitation of the nucleus.

to produce a nucleus of carbon[14] and an energetic proton. Thus a nonenergetic neutron will have a biological effect equivalent to an energetic gamma ray, or to an energetic proton plus an energetic carbon[14] ion.

In summary, all particles, charged or not, have a similar action on matter. Directly or indirectly, they produce excited atoms, molecules, and ion pairs. These processes always occur in practically the same proportions, and therefore the number of ion pairs formed can be used as a measure of the radiation effects. The more ion pairs produced in living matter, the greater the extent of biological damage. For this reason it is customary to describe radiation effects in terms of the number of ion pairs created per gram of living tissue in various parts of the body. Since each ion pair corresponds to an energy transfer of about 32 electron-volts, an alternative description may be given in terms of the amount of energy deposited. The unit in common usage for this purpose is the *roentgen,* which means specifically an energy equivalent to lifting the body (in which the radiation is deposited) by one twenty-fifth of an inch. This is equivalent to about 60 million million ion pairs in each ounce. It is less exact but more significant to say that one roentgen deposits in a cell of our body a few thousand ion pairs.

Of course the amount of ionization within individual cells is not a quantity that is easily measured. What one usually knows instead, is the roentgen dosage to a piece of tissue, which consists of many cells. If the charged particles inducing the ionization are electrons (as they are when the primary radiation is a beta ray or a gamma ray), the ionization will be distributed more or less uniformly among the cells in the affected neighborhood. If the charged particle is heavy—a proton or an alpha ray—the density of ionization which it produces is much greater, so that some cells receive a good many more ion pairs, while others nearby may receive none. For this reason it is sometimes important to specify not just how many roentgens the tissue has been exposed to, but also which kind of radiation has been responsible.

In a later chapter we shall discuss the biological effects of various amounts of radiation. We may mention here, however, that 1000 roentgens of X-rays or gamma rays delivered more or less uniformly over the whole body of a human being in a time less than a few hours or so, will lead to almost certain death. And it is a remarkable fact that nature has not provided us with a warning. Radiation does not hurt. The greater is the need that we understand this process which affects our well-being but not our senses.

CHAPTER IX

The Test

TESTING OF atomic explosives is usually carried out in beautiful surroundings. There is a good reason for this: the radioactive fallout.

Because of the fallout, the test site must be isolated. The presence of human population does not improve nature (with exceptions which are quite rare and the more notable). Also, to keep the site clean, tests must be carried out in the absence of rain. Therefore, at the site one usually finds sunshine and solitude.

For the participants the beauty of nature forms the backdrop to preparations of experiments which are difficult and exciting to everyone involved. At the end, the atomic explosion is always dwarfed by its setting. But the work that culminates in the detonation is rewarded by something quite different from a flash and a bang.

The really important results of a test consist in marks on photographic plates. Most of the apparatus that produced the plates has been destroyed in the explosion. But enough is saved so that one can conclude what has happened in the short fractions of a second that pass between the pressing of the button and the knowledge in the observer: this was it. In those fractions of a second another stone was added to the structure which we may call astrophysical engineering. What happens and what is observed in nuclear explosions are closely related to the behavior of matter in the interiors of the stars.

The details of the nuclear explosion cannot be described here for three reasons. First, the details are secret. Second, the size of this book and the forebearance of the reader set limitations. And third, we understand only a small part of the process. Within these limitations, this is what happens:

The actual nuclear reaction takes only a fraction of a microsecond (one microsecond = one millionth of a second). All the energy of the bomb is released in this short period. At the end of this period, the main body of the nuclear material is moving apart at a rapid rate and by this motion further nuclear reactions are stopped. In addition to the more or less orderly outward motion, considerable portions of the energy are found in the disorderly temperature motion, which has stripped most of the electrons off the nuclei and has transformed the atoms into a freely and chaotically moving assembly of charged particles. By this time many of the original nuclei have been transformed into nuclei of radioactive species, partly by the fission process and partly by the capture of neutrons in all sorts of atoms which had been originally present in the bomb materials.

Still another portion of the energy is present as electromagnetic radiation. This radiation closely resembles light except that it is of shorter wave length and is therefore not actually visible; but it can be absorbed and re-emitted by all sorts of materials, and is in a violent exchange of energy with the exploded bomb fragments.

All this perturbation spreads outward from the region where the nuclear reaction has taken place into the surrounding components of the bomb. During the outward spread, more atoms and more space get engulfed. The agitation and the radiation become somewhat less hot.

This hot region tends to be limited by a sharply defined boundary which is called a shock front and which is moving outward at a speed of several hundred miles per second. This front finally reaches the limits of the more or less dense material in which the whole bomb structure was originally encased. It then breaks through into the surrounding air. The air heats up in the immediate vicinity, and this is the beginning of the fireball.

From this point on, the energy spreads due to the push of the high-temperature air. A sharp shock front forms and keeps moving outward at a speed greatly surpassing ordinary sound speed. The radioactive material is contained within this hot and expanding sphere.

As the fireball expands and the temperature falls, more and more visible radiation is emitted. Actually, the surface is growing less brilliant as the structure expands and cools, but its greater size and the longer time that is available for the emission of radiation overcome this disadvantage. Finally, at a radius of perhaps a few hundred feet for a small bomb and a mile for a big one, the fireball expansion halts. This happens because the shock front is no longer strong enough to make the air luminous. The luminosity not only stops advancing but is actually partly dimmed by absorbing substances formed by the badly mistreated air molecules.

The time which has elapsed to reach this stage of the explosion depends on the bomb energy. If two explosions are compared, and the bigger one has a thousand times the explosive power of the smaller one, then the time needed to reach the extreme expansion of the fireball will be approximately ten times greater for the more violent event. In any case, a reasonably close observer has to use strongly absorbing glasses during this time if he is not to be blinded. For small bombs, the expansion of the fireball is too short to register.

For the really big ones, you can see the expansion developing and you wonder when it will stop. To the unprotected eye the small bombs are almost as dangerous as the big ones, because there is not enough time to blink.

In the meantime, the shock wave, now separated from the fireball, travels through the air and carries with it a considerable fraction of the original explosive power. An important part of the damage which a bomb can cause is due to this invisible pressure wave which spreads with a speed close to that of sound, over a distance of miles, before it settles down into harmless rumbling.

The rest of the energy is still sitting in the fireball near the point where the explosion occurred and the hot air now commences to ascend, breaking up into a turbulent mushroom as it goes. The hot interior portions get occasionally exposed and the object gives the appearance of an enormous flaming mass, at least when seen in a motion picture which slows down the action and reduces the size. The radiant tongues are too big and too fast for any ordinary flames.

During this stage the display gradually pales sufficiently so that it can be viewed with the naked eye. The originally hot masses have now emitted enough energy in the form of light and mixed with a sufficiently great mass of cool air that they no longer glow violently. This mass of central and rising gas contains practically all the radioactivity, not only that originally formed in the explosion but also some produced by neutrons which leaked out of the bomb and got captured by a variety of nuclei in the air, water, or ground within the neighborhood.

And now the aftermath of the explosion is turning into a display growing rapidly and yet in a measured manner so that not only the eye of the observer but his mind and his feelings can follow the events. The mushroom which has been formed by the first updraft develops into a column with more and more agitated boiling masses added on the top and with slanting skirts of a snowy appearance descending toward the sides. What is this white mass that looks just like a cloud of peculiar shape and that has grown up to the high heavens (or as the meteorologists call it: the stratosphere) in a few minutes before our eyes?

It is actually a cloud: a collection of droplets of water too small to turn into rain but big enough to reflect the white light of the sun. And it is formed in a similar way to the cumulus clouds of a thunderstorm. Indeed it is a beautiful example of a many-storied castle of cumulus upon cumulus. But strangely enough what makes this cloud is not the heat of the bomb. It is the cooling of the air masses that have been sucked in as the remnants of the fireball rush upward like a giant balloon. Under this balloon air is drawn upward. As this air rises, it cools and water vapor contained in it condenses into droplets: precisely the same mechanism which gives rise to thunderheads on a hot summer day.

The white skirts (which are not always present) do not consist of any material that is falling out of the cloud. On the contrary, a moist layer of air is sucked up into the cloud from the side and the droplets which form in this layer give rise to a cloud-sheet with the appearance of a skirt.

In big bombs near the top a particularly smooth and white cap is seen. This is again condensation, not into droplets but into fine crystals of ice. In some explosions more than one of these caps are present.

Finally the cloud has gained its full height. Depending on the size of the bomb it may have grown to 20,000 feet, to 100,000 feet or more. Then the wind blowing at various levels in various directions tears the structure apart sweeping some of it to the east, some to the west. The radioactive debris in the cloud has started on its travel.

What this radioactivity will do, how it can affect living beings, how dangerous it actually is, we shall discuss in succeeding chapters. But one thing is clear and remains present in the minds of all participants in an atomic test: The danger of the test is nothing compared to the catastrophe that may occur if great numbers of these weapons should be used in an unrestricted nuclear war.

It has been frequently asserted that our present atomic explosives can wipe out the cities and industries of the greatest countries. Why continue with further development and testing?

The answer is simple: The main purpose of a war is not to destroy the enemy's civilian centers but rather to defeat his armed forces, and for this purpose we need flexible refined weapons of all kinds and sizes. We also need weapons with which to defend our own cities. We need weapons with which to defend our allies and in particular we need weapons which will do their job against an aggressor and will do the least possible damage to the innocent bystander.

In this last respect, in particular, notable progress has been made. We are developing clean weapons which are effective by their blast and their heat, but which produce little radioactivity. Of course, blast and heat will do damage only near the point of detonation. Radioactivity may be carried by the winds and escape the control of man to a considerable extent.

It is clear that war is and always has been terrible. We refuse to believe that wars will always be with us but we cannot disregard the danger of war as long as the world is half free and half slave.

An atomic war, limited or even unlimited, need not be connected with more suffering than past wars. However, such a war would probably be more violent and it would be shorter.

The story is told that a war which turned out to be perhaps the most dreadful in the history of mankind was started with this message: "Thou hast chosen war. That will happen which will happen and what is to be we know not. God alone knows." Perhaps the only possible path for a free people is to be well prepared for war but never to choose war as long as the choice is free. But what will happen God alone knows.

which will happen and where; then we know now. And along
comes--" Perhaps the only possible technique may people is
to be well prepared for war, but never to choose war so long
as the choice is free. And what will happen God alone knows.

CHAPTER X

The Radioactive Cloud

IN FEBRUARY 1954 preparations were made on
Bikini Atoll for the explosion of a hydrogen bomb. March 1
was the "ready" date. It did not seem probable that the shot
would actually be fired on that date because the shot could
be fired only under quite favorable wind conditions. Large
amounts of radioactivity, especially fission products, were
expected from the explosion. The shot could be fired only if
no inhabited places lay in th downwind direction.

Bikini is an oval-shaped coral reef, an atoll. It is one of
several such atolls belonging to the group called the Marshall
Islands. If you look at the map, you will see that west of
Bikini at a distance of 200 miles lies Eniwetok, on which our
people were making preparations for further tests.

To the east of Bikini, a hundred miles or so, is Rongelap
Atoll. At that time 64 people were living there. They lived
primitively in palm houses on the southern part of the atoll.
The northern part was uninhabited.

On nearby Ailinginae Atoll 18 of the Marshallese islanders were on a fishing expedition, while farther to the east on
Rongerik 28 American servicemen were stationed. The serv-

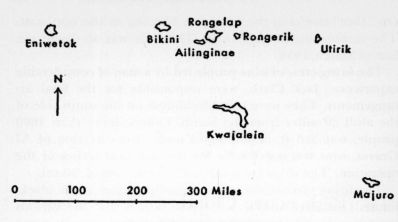

Map of the Marshall Islands

icemen lived and worked in aluminum huts. Their main job was to collect weather data.

Much farther to the east, 300 miles from Bikini, is Utirik. One hundred and fifty-seven Marshallese people lived on this atoll.

Early on the morning of March 1, a Japanese fishing boat lay somewhere to the north of Rongelap. Her name was Fukuryu Maru, which means in English the Fortunate Dragon. There were 23 men on board. Actually she was in a patrolled zone but had not been sighted by the patrol aircraft.

Operations for the test were being directed from ships of Joint Task Force 7. For several days prior to the morning of March 1, the weathermen had been mapping the winds. A wind to the west would be bad for Eniwetok. A wind to the east might hurt Rongelap and Rongerik. A wind to the south could affect Kwajalein. The ideal direction would have been due north, but this probably would not happen for months.

On "shot" morning the wind was blowing to the northeast. The meteorologists gave their "O.K." It was at dawn, the first of March, 1954.

The firing crew of nine people led by a man of considerable experience, Jack Clark, were responsible for the final arrangements. They were in a blockhouse on the south side of the atoll 20 miles from the bomb. Others, more than 1000 people, watched from shipboard under the direction of Al Graves, who was responsible for the technical phases of the operation. The ships lay south and a little east of Bikini.

The firing mechanism was set into operation in the blockhouse. One after another signals indicated that the various experiments and observations were set to work. Finally a red light went off and a green light appeared on the panel. This meant that the bomb had been detonated.

The men on shipboard watched the enormous fireball through darkened glasses. The firing crew, sealed off in the blockhouse, saw nothing. A couple of long seconds and Graves' voice announced over their radio: "It was a good shot." A quick estimate indicated 15 megatons.

Some more slow seconds and the expected ground shock arrived. It was like a big earthquake. A bad moment passed. The blockhouse rocked but held.

Another minute or so and the air shock passed over. One could hear the hinges groan—but this was no longer frightening.

Would the water wave pour over the blockhouse? Everything was watertight. After fifteen minutes a porthole was opened—no water came in. The men in the blockhouse emerged to look at the drifting atomic cloud.

While they watched, Jack Clark's radiation instrument began to show a reading. The firing crew was called back into the blockhouse. There, in the lowest corner shielded by a considerable amount of sand, they were safe. Outside, the evaporated and condensing coral came down in pellets carrying more and more radioactivity.

In the meantime there was fallout on the ships too. The wind had definitely veered after shot time. Quickly the activity was washed down. No one got a dangerous exposure. But it was wiser to sail away. A message was sent to the blockhouse: "We will come back for you in the evening."

After a little more than an hour the activity around the blockhouse started slowly to decrease. The firing crew waited patiently inside without communication, without light for the rest of the day.

Finally the ships came back. At sundown a helicopter went out to the island using the last of daylight and allowing as much time as possible for the activity to decay. Clark and his friends rushed out of the blockhouse wrapped in sheets to stop the beta rays and keep off the radioactive dust. They moved as fast as possible to avoid unnecessary exposure.

It was a hard experience but they got no more than two roentgens—no more reason to worry than if they had had a medical X-ray. Toward the east, however, some people were in real trouble.

Six or seven hours after the shot the American servicemen on Rongerik noticed a mistlike fallout of highly radioactive dust. The wind had veered enough to carry the atomic cloud over the occupied islands of Ailinginae, Rongelap, and Rongerik. In the anxious hours which followed no one could say how much damage had been done.

The Americans on Rongerik had had some education in the dangers of radioactivity. They washed themselves, put on extra clothes, and remained inside of the aluminum huts as much as possible. These actions helped to protect them against beta ray burns on the skin. The Marshallese on Rongelap and Ailinginae knew nothing of the danger and took no precautions. Many of them suffered quite severe skin burns.

All of the exposed persons were evacuated to Kwajalein as soon as the Task Force facilities would permit. But it was not until a week or so after the explosion that arrangements could be made for men with radiation measuring instruments to tour the atolls and determine what the levels of exposure had been.

On the southern tip of Rongerik they measured the activity and calculated that the American servicemen had received approximately 78 roentgens. This was good news because a dosage of 50 to 100 roentgens is not lethal and only in rare cases leads to any sickness. In any event full recovery could be expected within a few days.

As they prowled around Rongerik atoll, the measuring crew found places where the radiation levels had been much higher. At the northern end a person would have received more than 200 roentgens.

On Ailinginae the measured values were comparable to those on Rongerik. The estimated dosage to the Ailinginae people was 69 roentgens.

On Rongelap the situation was much worse. Measurements in the southern part of the atoll showed that the Rongelap people had gotten a dose of about 175 roentgens. Such a dose would not be fatal, but at least some of the people would probably be sick.

The crew then went on to explore the rest of the atoll. As they moved north, the dose levels rose higher and higher. In the middle of the atoll, only ten or fifteen miles from the inhabited part, a person would have received 400 roentgens of radiation. At this level he would have a fifty-fifty chance of surviving.

On the northern tip of the atoll, about thirty miles away, the dose would have been over a thousand roentgens. Such a dose means certain death in less than a month.

The following table contains a summary of what happened:

	Number of persons	Time of fallout after shot (hours)	Time of evacuation after shot (hours)	Dose (roentgens)
Rongelap	64	4 to 6	51	175
Ailinginae	18	4 to 6	58	69
Rongerik	28	7	32	78
Utirik	157	22	65	14
Fortunate Dragon	23	4		200

On Kwajalein the Marshallese were cared for and underwent medical observation. As soon as possible their skin and hair were scrubbed with soap and water. The coconut oil in their hair made decontamination difficult.

During all this time the presence of the Japanese fishing boat in the area was not even suspected. Not until two weeks after the explosion, when the little boat returned to Yaizu harbor, did the world find out. By this time the 23 fishermen were pretty sick. We do not know precisely what dose the fishermen received, but the best guess is about 200 roentgens. Unhappily, one of the fishermen died, presumably from complications associated with the exposure to radiation.[1] The other 22, however, are in good health and back at work.

Our medical information on the Marshallese islanders is complete. After staying three months on Kwajalein they were removed to Majuro atoll, where homes were built for them and where they have been cared for and under continuous surveillance since the incident. Frequent and thorough medical examinations have been conducted, handicapped somewhat by the problem of communicating through an interpreter.

In the first twenty-four hours some of the victims complained of nausea, fever, and stomach-ache. But these symptoms abated promptly in every case without treatment. There was also some complaint of skin itching and a burning sensation, but these symptoms also lasted only a couple of days.

[1] There seems to be a good possibility that he died from a hepatitis entirely unrelated to the initial radiation exposure.

Then followed a week or so of comfort and no complaint. After that skin lesions and loss of hair began to occur.

Fifty to eighty per cent of the beta rays during the exposure period had an average energy of 0.3 million electron-volts. Much of this energy was stopped in the outer layer of skin, which is two thousandths of an inch thick. The remainder of the beta rays had an average energy of 0.6 million electron-volts; these beta rays could easily penetrate into the deeper layer of live skin. The most important fact, however, was that clothing of any kind, even a thin cotton fabric, provided protection against all the beta rays. Lesions developed only on the exposed parts of the body and in a few other places such as the armpits and the creases of the neck where material tends to accumulate. Bare feet were especially bad. During the acute period some of the people walked on their heels.

At the end of six months lost hair had grown out again unaltered in texture and color, and the skin lesions had healed. Everyone appeared healthy and normal with no apparent after effects.

There had been four pregnancies amongst Rongelap women at the time of the exposure. One baby was born dead, but the other three were quite normal. There was no evidence that the stillbirth had been due to radiation effects. In fact the percentage of stillbirths amongst the Rongelapese is normally high. Statistically, one in four is not an unusual ratio.

Today, more than three years since the accident, all of the Marshallese and American victims seem to be fully recovered. No malignancies or leukemias have shown up, but these long-term effects are still being carefully watched for by an AEC medical group.

All in all some serious but limited harm has been done. It was a close shave. To see how close, one only needs to glance at the map below, which shows the roentgen dosage for 48 hours of exposure. At the southern tip of Rongelap, where the inhabitants lived, the dosage was 175 roentgens. But at the northern tip, less than thirty miles away, the dosage was more than a thousand roentgens. If the wind had veered just

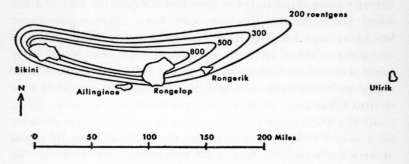

Dosage in First 48 Hours After Fallout Began

a little bit farther to the south, probably all of the people on Ailinginae, Rongelap, and Rongerik would have been killed.

This shot proved what had been argued for many years: that radioactivity is not just an incidental part of an atomic explosion. The people on Rongelap were far outside the area of danger from blast and thermal effects. But they received a sizeable dose of radiation. In fact, a person could have stood unprotected at a distance of thirty miles from the explosion and been perfectly safe from the blast and thermal radiation. But at that same distance in a downwind direction he would have accumulated a lethal dose of radiation within a matter of minutes after the fallout began.

Because of the radioactive fallout, the test sites must be located in remote parts of the world. It would be desirable if sites could be found which are so remote from populous areas that the tests could be conducted without regard to the direction of the winds. Unfortunately the bombs are too big and the planet is too small.

As a result the winds must be watched before every test; and the tests must be delayed until the winds are favorable. What happened to the Marshallese was an accident which might have been avoided if the winds had been blowing more directly toward the north at shot time. Since this accident the wind requirements for the tests have become far more stringent, our knowledge of the danger has increased, and the rules of safety have in all respects improved. Many large yield weapons have been tested since March 1, 1954, but no other accidents have occurred. We can be confident that accidents of this kind are now very improbable.

At the U. S. test site in Nevada there has been no instance of a major fallout on a populated area. Probably the most worrisome situation which has occurred there was in the spring of 1953 during the Upshot-Knothole test series. After the ninth shot of the series the cloud drifted eastward over St. George, Utah, a town of about 5000 people. Some fallout occurred shortly before nine o'clock in the morning. About nine-thirty AEC officials issued a warning advising the residents to stay indoors. By noon the warning was withdrawn and people were allowed to continue with their normal affairs. The incident left everyone a little bit scared, but no one had received a radiation dose greater than two or three roentgens.

We have been talking about the local fallout which occurs within a few hundred miles of the test site. Not all the radioactivity which is made in the explosion goes into this fallout. Some of it travels for really long distances, not hundreds but actually thousands of miles from ground zero. This part of the radioactivity is disseminated world-wide and completely escapes the control of man. To be sure, by the time this radioactivity is distributed over a large fraction of the earth's surface, the dosage levels of radiation are very tiny, less than a ten thousandth of a roentgen for a megaton explosion. There is no danger whatever that a person would die or even become mildly sick from this amount of radiation. There is, however, the possibility of long-range effects such as bone cancer, leukemia, and genetic mutation.

The world-wide danger is, of course, primarily due to the big bombs. The little ones, such as are tested in Nevada, release about ten kilotons (TNT equivalent) of fission energy. Some of the big ones in the Pacific release a few megatons of fission energy. Since the amount of radioactivity is proportional to the fission energy released, one big bomb is equivalent to several hundred or possibly a thousand little ones. Altogether in Nevada, to date, there have been only sixty or seventy shots. It may be desirable to minimize the world-wide fallout from the big shots in the Pacific. But for the little shots in Nevada, it is probably more important to minimize the local fallout. How much radioactivity goes into the local fallout, how much into the world-wide, and how these relative amounts can be controlled, are the main topics for the remainder of this chapter.

Not all the radioactivity which is made in the explosion contributes to the fallout, either local or world-wide. Some of the radioactive fission fragments (gamma emitters) have such short half-lives[2] that they actually disintegrate before the bomb has disassembled. A great many others disintegrate in the first few minutes while the atomic cloud is rising. The energetic beta and gamma rays released in these early, rapid disintegrations are stopped in short distances and merely add to the havoc at the scene of the explosion.

For the radioactivity to affect areas at a large distance from the point of the explosion, considerable time must elapse while the atomic cloud rises and drifts in the horizontal winds. During this time more disintegrations occur, due mainly to the short-lived nuclei. The rate at which they oc-

[2] Half-lives of radioactive nuclei are uninfluenced by the extreme temperatures or pressures of the explosion, or by the state of motion of the particles or where they happen to be.

1. A shallow underground explosion. The radioactivity and the ground dirt are thoroughly mixed.

USAEC—Joint Office of Test Information

2. An atomic test tower— five hundred feet high.

USAEC—Lookout Mountain Laboratory, USAF

3. A tower shot. Ground dirt rises along the stem, but very little actually mixes with the fireball.

4. An air shot—3,500 feet above ground. No dirt.

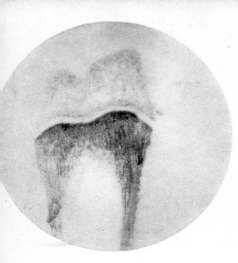

5. Leg bone of a three-month-old rabbit killed ten minutes after injection of Sr^{89}. The darkened areas show where the strontium has been deposited. Sr^{90} and normal Sr^{88} would be deposited in the same places. It is an important fact that the deposition is fairly uniform in the calcified portions of the bone.

From a chapter by Vaughan, Tutt, and Kidman in the book Biological Hazards of Atomic Energy, *edited by Haddow, published by Oxford University Press, 1952*

Leg bone of a woman ho died of radium poi- ning. The bright re- ons show where the dium has been de- osited. Hot spots are early visible.

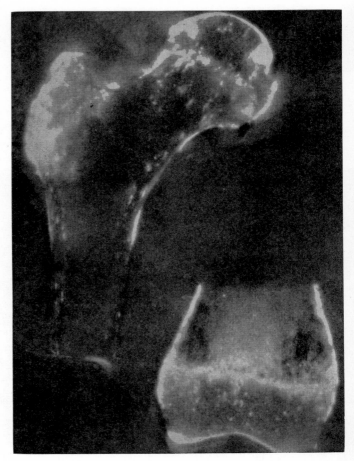

rom an article, "The Late ffects of Internally De- osited Radioactive Ma- rials in Man," by Aub al., in Medicine—a pro- ssional journal, Vol. 31, o. 3, September, 1952

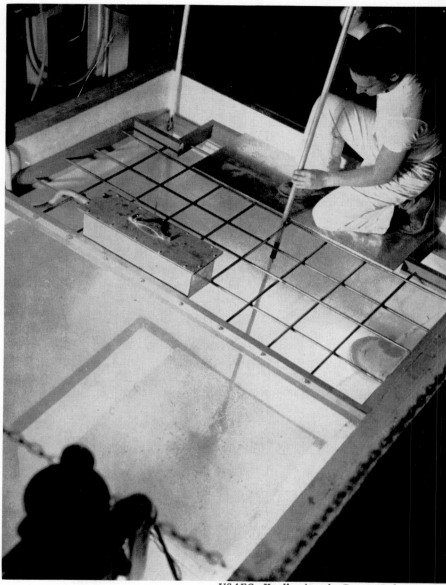

USAEC—Knolls Atomic Power Laboratory

7. Capsules of cobalt[60], shielded in a water tank. One hundred and thirty million dollars' worth of radium, twice the world's present supply, would be needed to equal the rays from this powerful gamma source.

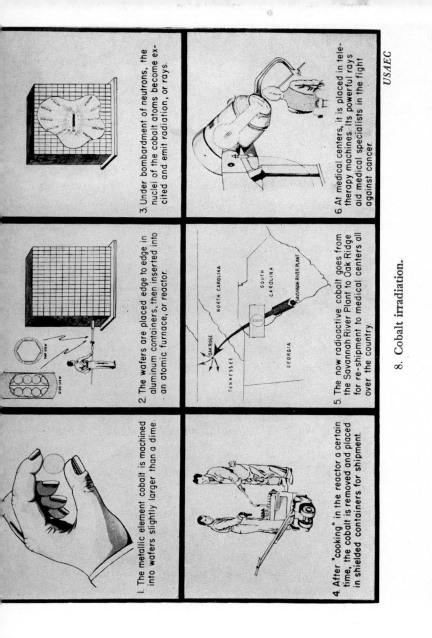

1. The metallic element cobalt is machined into wafers slightly larger than a dime.

2. The wafers are placed edge to edge in aluminum containers, then inserted into an atomic furnace, or reactor.

3. Under bombardment of neutrons, the nuclei of the cobalt atoms become excited and emit radiation, or rays.

4. After "cooking" in the reactor a certain time, the cobalt is removed and placed in shielded containers for shipment.

5. The now radioactive cobalt goes from the Savannah River Plant to Oak Ridge for re-shipment to medical centers all over the country.

6. At medical centers, it is placed in tele-therapy machines. Its powerful rays aid medical specialists in the fight against cancer.

USAEC

8. Cobalt irradiation.

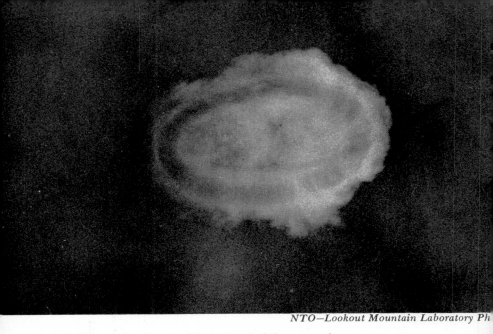

NTO—*Lookout Mountain Laboratory Ph*

9. The smoke-ring cloud from the air-defense atomic weapon.

10. *Wide World Ph*

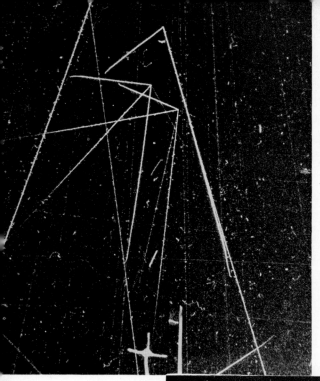

11. The streaks are condensation trails produced by charged particles in a Wilson Cloud Chamber. They appear bright because the chamber is illuminated and the condensation trails reflect light just as an ordinary cloud does.

12. Another picture in the Wilson Cloud Chamber. A large number of closely-spaced tracks form a cloud. (The tracks are curved because of the presence of a magnetic field.)

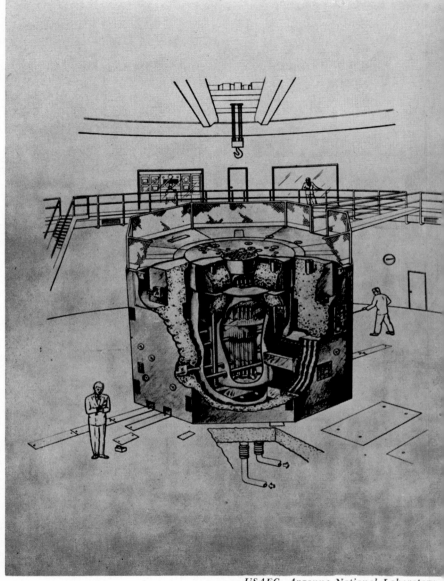

USAEC—Argonne National Laboratory

13. Cutaway section of a nuclear reactor. The heart of the reactor is a small region at the center where the fission energy is generated. Most of the weight and volume are needed for cooling apparatus and shielding material to keep in nuclear radiation.

cur keeps diminishing as the short-lived nuclei disappear. Roughly speaking, the rate diminishes simply in proportion to the time. More precisely, the rate drops somewhat faster, decreasing by a factor of ten when the time increases by a factor of seven. A minute after the explosion the activity is less than one per cent of what it is at a second. After an hour it is less than one per cent of its value at a minute. This law for the decrease in activity of fission products is, of course, quite different from the simple law of radioactive decay. The latter law applies to a single radioactive species. The fission products consist at any instant of many different radioactive species. Each one obeys the simple law of radioactive decay, but the totality follows a different law.

It should be kept in mind that the product nucleus of a radioactive disintegration may itself be radioactive with a different half-life. For example, there is strontium^{90}. Only a small amount of this isotope is made directly in the fission process. The fission process yields large quantities of krypton^{90}, which decays with a half-life of one-half minute into rubidium^{90}. The latter has a half-life of three minutes and decays into strontium^{90}. This is how practically all of the strontium^{90} is made in the explosion. Thus both the intensity and the nature of the radioactivity keep changing with time.

These facts are important because they determine the magnitude and the character of the danger when the radioactivity finally falls out of the cloud and is deposited on the surface of the earth. Those radioactive particles which disintegrate while still in the cloud need not worry us since this radiation can have no effect on living organisms that may be underneath. Provided that the cloud is more than a few hundred feet above the ground, the beta and gamma rays released in these disintegrations merely dissipate their energy in ionizing the air.

The time which the radioactive debris spends in the cloud depends most critically on one factor: the proximity of the explosion to the ground surface. The nature of the surface, whether it is soil or water, also plays a role. If the explosion has taken place right on the ground, on a soil surface, a lot of big, heavy dirt particles become incorporated into the fireball and begin to fall under the action of gravity even before the cloud stops rising. This fallout continues for a period of several hours to perhaps a half day. At the same time some of the radioactive fission products which have adhered to these dirt particles also fall out. This is the origin of the so-called close-in or local fallout, which extends for a distance downwind of the explosion of a few miles to a few hundred miles, according to the energy of the bomb and the strength of the winds. Approximately eighty per cent or so of all the fission products are accounted for by this close-in fallout in the case of a surface explosion. The shot on March 1, 1954 was of this variety.

There are several possibilities for influencing the amount of close-in fallout. One is to explode the bomb over deep water. In this case the close-in fallout amounts to between thirty and fifty per cent. This is because many of the water drops to which radioactive particles have adhered evaporate before they hit the ground. Over shallow water, however, if the fireball actually touches the bottom, the close-in fallout resembles the case of a land explosion and is again about eighty per cent or so. The close-in fallout for underground or underwater explosions will be even higher than for the surface explosions. In fact a really deep underground or underwater explosion would be completely contained and no activity would be spread around.

Another possibility for reducing the close-in fallout is to detonate the bomb on a tower so tall that the fireball cannot touch the surface. In this case the amount of close-in fallout is reduced from eighty per cent to approximately five per cent. Of course, it is not feasible to build towers for really big bombs whose fireballs may be a mile or so in diameter. In this case the bomb might be dropped from an airplane to produce the same effect. The Hiroshima explosion was an example of an air burst of a small bomb. The close-in fallout in that case was very small. Such radiation sickness as occurred there was due to the direct gamma rays and neutrons released in the explosion itself.

In the case of a near-surface explosion, where the fireball almost touches the ground, the close-in fallout is also only about five per cent. This is a somewhat surprising fact since in this case photographs show large quantities of surface material being sucked up into the cloud, just as they are in a true surface explosion.

This material certainly consists of large, heavy dirt particles which subsequently fall out of the cloud. Yet most of them somehow fail to come in contact with the radioactive fission products.

This peculiar phenomenon can be understood by looking at the details of how the fireball rises. At first the central part of the fireball is much hotter than the outer part and thus rises more rapidly. As it rises, however, it cools and falls back around the outer part, creating in this way a doughnut-shaped structure. The whole process is analogous to the formation of an ordinary smoke ring. In most of the photographs one sees, the doughnut is obscured by the cloud of water that forms, but sometimes when the weather is particularly dry, it becomes perfectly visible. During the rather orderly circulation of air through the hole, the bomb debris and the dirt that has been sucked up remain separated. (See pictures 1-4.)

The close-in fallout accounts for only a portion of the radioactivity, ranging from less than a per cent for a high altitude shot to almost complete deposition for some ground shots. For the world-wide fallout we are interested in what happens to the remainder. This depends on how the atomic cloud is carried by the upper winds for long distances. In this connection it is important to distinguish between a big bomb and a little bomb. It is also important to distinguish between the lower and higher portions of the atmosphere called, respectively, the troposphere and the stratosphere.

The atmosphere is heated by the sun in an indirect way. The sun's rays pass through air without warming it. They heat up instead the bottom of the atmosphere, that is, the solid ground. The atmosphere is heated in the same manner in which a boiling pot is heated on the kitchen range. The heat is delivered from below and is carried in rising currents to the top.

Only in the case of the atmosphere there is no sharp upper limit. The currents rise to an altitude of thirty to fifty thousand feet, then turn and descend. This boiling part of the atmosphere is called the troposphere or region of heat. Above it there is less vertical motion. The upper region is called the stratosphere or stratified region.

For a little bomb the atomic cloud stops rising before it reaches the stratosphere. For a big bomb, above about a megaton of energy (a million tons of TNT equivalent), the cloud pokes right into the stratosphere and keeps going to a height of a hundred thousand feet or so.

The most important fact about the stratosphere is this: It has very little weather. Most of the weather phenomena such as clouds, rain, snow, fog, mist, etc., are confined to the lower portion of the atmosphere, the troposphere. The stratosphere, however, contains practically no water.

Now suppose a little bomb whose cloud will remain in the troposphere has been exploded at one of the United States test sites. The Nevada test site is at a latitude of 37°N and the Pacific test site at 12°N. In these middle latitudes, in the troposphere, the winds blow mainly from west to east with an average speed of approximately 20 miles an hour. There will be a slight southerly or northerly motion on top of this. But by and large the radioactive cloud will stay in a pretty narrow band around the latitude at which the explosion took place.

After the first few hours, when the close-in fallout has dwindled, the radioactive particles remaining in the cloud are too light and too fine to fall any more under the action of gravity. At this point the weather becomes important. Rain, fog, or mist captures the radioactive particles, and returns them to the ground in the rainfall. This results in the so-called tropospheric fallout.[3] The average time for this fallout to occur is approximately two weeks to a month. During this time, while staying more or less in the latitude of the explosion, the radioactive particles may actually have encircled the earth.

The clouds of the big bombs rise high into the stratosphere. The winds in the stratosphere do not blow so predominantly in a latitudinal direction. What is more important, they stay in the stratosphere for years, in which time the radioactivity is distributed to all areas of the globe. The fallout from the big bombs is thus really world-wide.

The tropospheric fallout takes about a month. The stratospheric fallout takes 5 to 10 years. The reason for this difference is the weather, or rather the lack of it. In the stratosphere there is no rain or fog to catch the radioactive particles and hence no effective mechanism for producing the fallout. In fact, since the radioactive particles are too fine to fall by gravity, they must simply wait until some turbulent motions impel them downward back into the troposphere. This process requires a long time.

That rainfall is the most important mechanism for producing the world-wide fallout has been shown by examining the fallout in certain dry regions of southern California and South America. In every case the fallout was found to be con-

[3] A small amount may drift down to the ground in the winds. This may get deposited on leaves and grass.

siderably sub-normal. In one place in Chile, where there is never any rain, the fallout was found to be only one per cent of what might be expected on the basis of the average fallout at the same latitude.

In regions having at least a few inches of rain per year, the fallout tends to be proportional to the rainfall on the average. However, the proportionality to rainfall depends on the nature of the weather so that, say, twenty inches of rain in one part of the world may not give as much fallout as the same amount of rain in other weather zones. We are rapidly learning about this.

Having said what the age is of the various kinds of fallout, we are in a position to say which radioactive species are still present when the radioactivity is deposited on the ground. The close-in fallout, being only a few hours old, still includes many short-lived isotopes, which disintegrate before there is a possibility of ingestion or inhalation into the body. Consequently the danger from the close-in fallout results from external exposure, mainly to gamma radiation on the whole body, and to a lesser extent to energetic beta rays on the skin. Clothes and ordinary housing provide relatively little shielding against gamma rays. Special protective shelters are needed. During a war if the enemy were to bomb our cities with super-megaton weapons surface-burst, the close-in fallout would be a far greater agent of destruction against an unsheltered populace than either blast or thermal radiation.

In the stratospheric world-wide fallout, however, all of the short-lived radioactivity has disappeared, since a period of many years has elapsed since the explosion. After a year or so the only gamma emitter which is left in appreciable quantity is cesium[137], with a half-life of 30 years. Its gamma ray, however, is not very penetrating. In spite of this fact cesium[137] is considered to be the second most important hazard for the long term fallout. The first is strontium[90], which is a beta emitter with a half-life of 28 years. This is long enough so that most of these nuclei will still be present even after spending a long time in the stratosphere. Since strontium is chemically similar to calcium, it contaminates our foodstuffs and is easily incorporated into our bodies. Once inside it stays for long periods of time, deposited in our bones. We shall see in a later chapter how serious this danger may be.

The tropospheric fallout, and to a lesser extent, the stratospheric, includes some other radioactive species besides cesium[137] and strontium[90], and we shall discuss these in the next chapter. But by and large they are of little consequence (with the possible exception of iodine[131]) either because they are not easily absorbed in the body or else because their radiation is not very energetic. The world-wide hazard is thus narrowed down to just two isotopes, an internal beta emitter and a weak gamma emitter.

CHAPTER XI

From the Soil to Man

THERE IS A bewildering variety of radioactive products deposited in the fallout. Given certain conditions all of them could be dangerous to man. Actually, very few are.

An example of a radioactive isotope which is produced in large quantity by the fission process and about which there is some reason to worry, but actually is not dangerous to man, is iodine[131]. This isotope in the fallout is not dangerous because it has a rather short half-life: eight days.

During the first weeks after a nuclear explosion some radioactive iodine may fall out of the cloud and contaminate grazing land. A cow eats hundreds of pounds of grass in a few days time. Now iodine is found in the cow's body or in the body of any mammal mainly in one spot. This is the thyroid gland located in man near the Adam's apple. The thyroid gland is important because it secretes a chemical which regulates many of the body functions. In man, these include how we burn up our food and in what mood we are. About twenty per cent of all the iodine which is taken up, whether radioactive or natural, is concentrated in this one rather small gland. Such a concentration is precisely the kind of danger for which we must watch.

Shortly after nuclear tests, cows that graze on range land have been found with abnormally large amounts of radioactive iodine, although not so large as to be harmful. In human beings, however, the measured levels of radioactive iodine are less than a hundredth of what they are in the cows because by the time this radioactive isotope has reached man, it has mostly decayed into a stable, harmless variety of xenon gas.

There are many potentially dangerous isotopes in the radioactive debris of a nuclear explosion. But most of them decay too soon to affect man.

Isotopes which live an extremely long time compared to the human life-span are also not dangerous to man. A radioactive particle in the body is not harmful unless it disintegrates and releases its energy while the individual is still alive.

Two examples of long-lived radioactive isotopes, which are used as fuel in the bombs and which may be left over from the explosion in large quantities, are: uranium^{235} and plutonium^{239}. Uranium^{235} has a half-life of 710 million years, which is much too long to be dangerous. Plutonium has a half-life of 24,000 years and is somewhat more dangerous. The danger from plutonium arises because it emits an energetic alpha ray.

The danger from radioactivity depends on the kind of particle emitted—alpha, beta, or gamma rays—and whether these rays attack the body from the inside or the outside. From the outside the gamma rays are the most dangerous and the alpha rays the least dangerous. From the inside the order is just reversed.

To cause damage from the outside the radiation must be very penetrating. Gamma rays can go through the whole body. Beta rays are stopped in the skin tissue. Alpha rays cannot even penetrate the outer layer of non-living, protective skin.

On the inside, however, in the sensitive organs, the short range of the alpha rays makes them exceedingly dangerous. Their energy is concentrated in a small amount of tissue to which damage is severe. The beta rays cause a slightly less concentrated damage, and the gamma rays the least concentrated of all.

Radioactivity may enter the body as contamination in the food we eat or in the air we breathe. To be dangerous, however, it must remain in the body, either in the intestines or the lungs or in other vital organs, long enough for disintegrations to occur, which will ionize and injure the living cells.

Fortunately, plutonium in our food is easily excreted from the body. Only a few thousandths of a per cent of what is eaten, is actually absorbed. If inhaled, large particles are stopped in the nasal passages. Small particles get into the lungs but are quickly exhaled. Only intermediate sized particles are absorbed. However, the plutonium which is absorbed generally gets laid down in the bones, where it stays for a long period of time. Altogether, plutonium in the small amounts we usually deal with is not one of the greater dangers to human beings. Perhaps its most disagreeable property is that, being an alpha emitter, it is not very easy to detect. Since alpha particles do not penetrate through the surface of most radiation meters, special instruments are needed to find them.

Two fission products which are readily absorbed upon ingestion are: strontium^{90} (Sr^{90}) and cesium^{137} (Cs^{137}). Depending somewhat on their chemical form, approximately thirty-five per cent of the Sr^{90} is absorbed, and all of the Cs^{137} is absorbed. Both of these isotopes are plentifully made in the fission process. Moreover they have very "dangerous" half-lives—about 30 years—which is long enough so that decay is negligible between the explosion and contact with man, but short enough so that decay is probable after contact.

From such arguments as these one concludes that Sr^{90} and Cs^{137} are the most important isotopes for the internal hazard from the world-wide fallout. One can be reasonably sure that there are no others of importance, because careful and extensive research has not found significant amounts of any in our bodies. We need not fear that one has been overlooked, because the beta activity of the fission products is always easy to detect.

The two main questions which we have to answer are these: In what precise way will the dangerous elements Sr^{90} and Cs^{137} be distributed in the body? And after they are distributed, what kind of damage will they produce?

We know too little about the chemistry of the living body to obtain a complete answer to the second question. Hence it has to be admitted that the actual danger cannot be stated in a precise way.

Fortunately, enough is known from direct experience to obtain a good value for the greatest damage that might be produced. In the present chapter we shall describe what is known about the uptake of the dangerous elements into the body. In following chapters we shall turn to the question of the biological consequences.

We may begin by comparing the danger from Cs^{137} with that from Sr^{90}. Both of these isotopes are made in the fission process in about equal numbers. (Roughly 2 or 2½ per cent of all the fission products are Sr^{90}, and 3 per cent Cs^{137}.) They have approximately the same radioactive half-lives. But they differ in an important respect: The Cs^{137} is deposited more or less uniformly throughout the body; the Sr^{90} is concentrated in the bones.

Cs^{137} emits a large part of its radioactive energy in the form of a gamma ray, which causes ionization uniformly in the body. Sr^{90}, on the other hand, emits all of its energy in the form of two beta rays, which have ranges of only a small fraction of an inch in the bone. Thus in the one case the radioactive disintegration energy is distributed in the whole body; in the other, the energy is deposited in the bones only.

Since the bones comprise about ten per cent of the total body weight, they are subjected to ten times the radiation dosage. The bones are quite sensitive to radiation, and an overdosage can cause bone cancer and interfere with the production of blood cells that goes on in the marrow. Thus we are led to the conclusion that Sr^{90} is a far greater potential hazard than Cs^{137}. A further point, which leads to the same conclusion, is that Cs^{137}, after being absorbed, is retained in the body less than six months and then excreted. Sr^{90} is retained for many years.

On the other hand, Cs^{137} can cause a type of damage which Sr^{90} cannot cause: namely, damage to the reproductive cells. The effect of Sr^{90} is indeed limited to the bones and adjacent or nearby bone marrow, and does not reach the reproductive organs. In a later chapter we shall take up the question of genetic danger, and then we shall be very interested in Cs^{137}. For the remainder of this chapter, however, we may focus our attention on Sr^{90}.

Since a large fraction of the Sr^{90} which enters the body stays there, the most important questions which remain are: how it gets there and how much gets there. The essential fact in this connection is that the Sr^{90} generally occurs in the fallout in a chemical form which is easily dissolved in water. The water is taken up by plants, by absorption through the leaves and the roots. Animals graze on the plants. Human beings eat the plants and drink the milk from the grazing animals, and thus become exposed to Sr^{90}. (See pictures 5 and 6.)

One might worry because Sr^{90} is not a naturally occurring isotope but has been made for the first time by man in the fission process. Here is an unfamiliar poison being scattered over the earth. Can we have any idea how much will be taken up by human beings?

The answer depends on a fact which we have emphasized throughout this book: that isotopes of the same element are chemically and biologically indistinguishable. The radioactive variety of strontium will behave exactly like the stable natural variety. In particular, the ratio of Sr^{90} to stable strontium in the human body must be the same as this ratio is in our food. From this premise we can predict how much Sr^{90} will reach the human body.

From the total yield of fission energy released in all nuclear tests to date, one can calculate exactly how much Sr^{90} has been produced. This amount turns out to be about 100 pounds.

Approximately one half of this amount has been deposited in and near the test sites in the close-in fallout. (Most of the radioactivity comes from the big bombs, and most of these have been burst on the ground or over shallow water.) A small portion of the 100 pounds has disintegrated in the cloud. The remainder, roughly 50 pounds, is partially still in the stratosphere and partially has been disseminated around the world in the tropospheric and stratospheric fallout. At the present time measurements show that 25 or 30 pounds have actually been returned to the surface of the earth. Local values vary from about one third to more than twice the average world-wide value.

In the northern part of the United States, in the regions of frequent rainfall, the measured values are about twice the world-wide average. In the latitudes between 10°S and 50°N the average value is about 50 per cent greater than the world-wide average. For the rest of the world one finds, with some variations, about one third the world-wide average.

Most of the Sr^{90} fallout is caught in the top two or three inches of the soil. It exists there in a water-soluble form that is readily assimilated by plants. Also in the soil, chemically inseparable from the Sr^{90}, is stable natural strontium. Plants, animals, and human beings have no way of distinguishing between the two.

It is not easy to determine how much natural strontium is in a form which is available to the plants. Some of the natural strontium is insoluble; and some is below the root depth. Our best estimate is that there are about 60 pounds per acre actually available for uptake by the plants. This is, of course, an average.

The amount of natural strontium in the human body is a quantity we know rather well. It has been carefully measured and is about 0.7 gram in the average adult, with proportionately less in children. Now since we know how greatly Sr^{90} has been diluted in the soil and how much natural strontium there is in our bodies, we can calculate the expected quantity of Sr^{90} in our bones. Considering the many uncertainties in the calculation one should not expect too good an agreement. The remarkable fact is that the quantity of Sr^{90} measured in small children does agree with the calculated amount. For adults the measured value is quite a bit less than the calculated amount because adult bones have been made for the most part before there was any Sr^{90} in the environment.

The fact that we can calculate how much Sr^{90} is at present in the body is most important because it gives us confidence that we understand what is happening. It is especially important for us to understand what is happening so that we can predict how nuclear tests which are carried out today will affect future levels of Sr^{90} in the body.

From arguments such as we have given, plus a record of the Sr^{90} content of bones over the last several years, it seems unlikely that the level of Sr^{90} will increase by more than a factor of two or so due to tests already conducted. Actually this factor may be even smaller both because of the mixing of the strontium with the deeper layers of the soil, and because the radioactive strontium which stays in the ground for a long time tends to become chemically less soluble and mixed more thoroughly with that part of the natural strontium which is chemically unavailable. This latter process is called "chemical aging."

To follow radioactive strontium and normal strontium from the soil into the food and the bones is not an easy matter. We must worry about the question of the strontium depth in the soil and the chemical form of the strontium. The complete identity of Sr^{90} and normal strontium holds only if both are near the same place and in the same chemical form. A further difficulty is that until recently little was known about the behavior of normal strontium and knowledge is accumulating slowly.

Much more is known about calcium. Now calcium and strontium do not behave in an identical way, but they do behave similarly. In passing from soil to man the ratio of calcium to strontium does not remain the same but at least it changes in a more or less definite manner. Actually most work on Sr^{90} uptake has been done by comparing Sr^{90} with calcium.

In order to use the data on calcium one has to find out how the calcium to strontium ratio is changed when the material is taken up into the human body. In the soil there is, on the average, about 1 part of strontium to 100 parts of calcium. In the human body the ratio is about 1 to 1400.

Thus the strontium is discriminated against relative to calcium in going from the soil to man by a factor of about 14. This is a factor of protection.

It is good to double-check this conclusion and to find out how the calcium to strontium ratio changes step by step in going from the soil to man. One finds a factor of 1.4 in going from the soil to the plant, a factor of 7 in going from the plant to the milk, and a factor of about 2 in going from the milk to man. Actually, if we put all these factors together we should expect that on the way from the soil to man the calcium to strontium ratio increases by a factor 20. This is in reasonable but not in excellent agreement with the ratio 14 given above.

Once the factor of protection is established we can get a value of the expected strontium uptake from the way in which the radioactive material is diluted by calcium rather than by normal strontium. This is a less straightforward but, for the time being, a more practical method than the direct Sr^{90}—normal strontium comparison. It is particularly important when one compares soils of rather different calcium content.

Plants and animals require calcium. When they do not get it, they develop a calcium-hunger. Since strontium is chemically similar to calcium, a lack of calcium in the soil is readily substituted by available strontium. One would expect that plants grown on calcium-poor soil and animals raised on such land would exhibit abnormally high natural strontium content and also a proportionately high Sr^{90} content. The high Sr^{90} content has in fact been verified. Some sheep in Wales, for example, appear to have about ten times the average amount of Sr^{90} in their bodies.

Fortunately most people derive their food from many areas widely separated from each other. Soil that is deficient in calcium is not likely to supply more than a small part of an individual's sustenance. However, the possibility of a large fluctuation cannot be ignored. In this event corrective measures would be needed. One simple measure would be to fertilize deficient soil with additional calcium.

That soil can be successfully treated in this way is illustrated by the present situation in Wales. The sheep with the abnormally high Sr^{90} content all come from the steep, poor pastures which are not limed. The sheep from the lower pastures, which are limed (not because of the fallout but for economic reasons), show an activity of only one third the value mentioned above.

The point we have tried to make in this chapter is that the present human levels of Sr^{90} can be satisfactorily accounted for by simple arguments based on the chemical similarity of elements and the identity of isotopes. These arguments give us confidence that we correctly understand how Sr^{90} and how much Sr^{90} is getting from the soil to the human body.

At the same time we have seen how many factors influence the eventual uptake into the human body: geographical latitude, frequency of rainfall, the chemical form in which strontium is found, the calcium content of the soil, the method of agriculture. Even though the United States has pushed this investigation vigorously since 1952 the bulk of the work is still ahead of us.

For instance, in the United States, dairy products provide most of the calcium and strontium in our diets. In Japan, however, the situation is somewhat different. There the main source of calcium and strontium is rice. As a result, the ratio of strontium to calcium may be passing differently from the soil to man. Also the fallout strontium might be washed deeper into the soil and the soluble to non-soluble ratio might be different.

Considering the complex nature of the Sr^{90} uptake into man, it is important to keep close track of the actual Sr^{90} levels in the soil, in our food, and in our own bodies. The following graphs show how these levels have risen in the last several years due to the bomb tests:

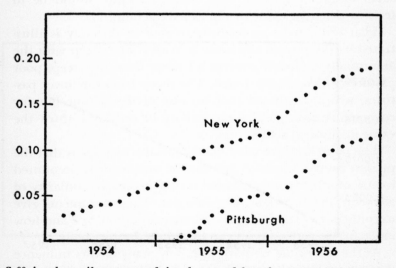

Sr^{90} in the soil—measured in thousandths of a gram per square mile.

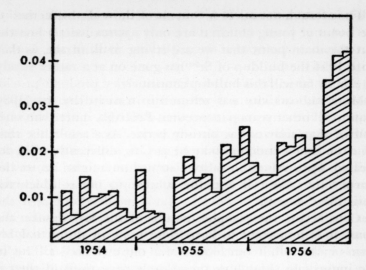

Average Sr[90] in U.S. milk—measured in trillionths of a gram per quart.

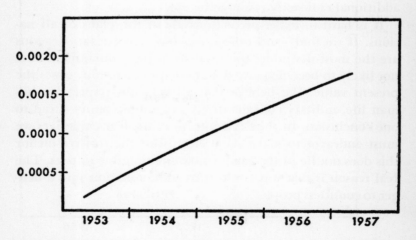

Average radiation doses from Sr[90] in bones of young children (U.S.)—measured in roentgens per year.

The actual amounts of Sr^{90} in the soil, in the milk, and in the bones of young children are only approximately known. But the main point that we are trying to illustrate, is that since 1954 the buildup of Sr^{90} has gone on at a rather steady rate. How far will this buildup continue?

More radioactivity was released in tests in the year 1954 than in all other years put together. Probably more than one-half of that activity has already been deposited. Since that time the fission energy produced in U.S. tests has steadily decreased. Furthermore, we have learned how to minimize the world-wide fallout by employing ground bursts which deposit most of their activity in the close-in fallout near the test site. It is also possible to place chemical additives near the bomb in order to convert the strontium into a more insoluble form or else into a form which will more readily fall out in the immediate neighborhood of the explosion. And what is most important—we are developing clean nuclear weapons, which produce blast and heat but greatly reduced radioactivity. In the future these clean weapons may eliminate the additional radioactivity altogether.

It is hard to make predictions about the plans of all nations. If we find—and others also find—that clean weapons are the most desirable, the total strontium contamination is not likely to become more than perhaps two to four times the present value. We believe that all reasons—respect for human life, military considerations and simple sanity—lead to one conclusion. In the development of nuclear explosives we must endeavor to make them clean. But the real reason for this does not lie in the small contamination due to tests. The real reason is that war could turn contamination into a danger to countless people.

CHAPTER XII

Danger to the Individual

How MUCH harm is being done by the atomic tests? Some scientists have claimed that from past tests alone about 50,000 persons throughout the world will die prematurely. There is no general agreement on this point. Some think the number should be smaller. It is possible that radioactivity produces some effects which prolong life rather than shorten it. But even if all the biological consequences of radiation were known many questions would still demand answers. Can tests be justified if they actually shorten some human lives? Even the possibility of a health hazard must be taken most seriously. On the other hand: Are there any reasons which make continued testing necessary?

We shall return to these questions in a later chapter. First, however, we shall try to put before the reader the known facts about the fallout danger to the individual. We shall try to put this danger into perspective by relating it to other more familiar dangers to which all of us are exposed. In the following chapter we shall discuss how the fallout may affect future generations.

The dangers from big doses of radiation are well known.

Exposure to a thousand roentgens over our whole body causes almost certain death in less than thirty days. Four or five hundred roentgens give a fifty-fifty chance of survival. At less than a hundred roentgens, there is no danger of immediate death. Three years ago the Marshallese got a dose of 175 roentgens. None died. Apparently all are in good health.

Over longer periods of time even bigger radiation doses can be tolerated. A thousand roentgens spread over a lifetime produce no apparent biological consequences in individual cases. A rough rule (which is not too well-established) is that five times as much radiation can be tolerated if one is exposed to only a little radiation at any one time.

A hundred roentgens all at once, or several times this amount over a protracted time period, will not cause sickness or death that can be directly blamed on the radiation. However, such a dose of radiation may have harmful biological consequences which are more subtle. An exposed individual may develop an increased susceptibility to certain diseases, notably bone cancer and leukemia. Leukemia is a fatal disease in which the white blood cells multiply too rapidly.

A person who receives a hundred roentgens does not necessarily contract bone cancer or leukemia. Rather, his chance of contracting these diseases during his lifetime may have been increased. Knowledge of this kind can be obtained only with the help of statistics.

If, for example, a large number of mice receive a heavy dosage of radiation over a long period of time, one finds that the incidence of tumors and leukemia is higher amongst such irradiated animals than the natural incidence of these diseases.

Direct evidence with human beings—fortunately—is rather scarce. Statistics exist on the survivors of Hiroshima and Nagasaki, and also on radiologists. The latter group probably receive several hundred roentgens during their professional lifetimes. In addition, some statistics exist on children who have been treated with large doses of radiation for enlarged thymuses. Persons suffering from ankylosing spondylitis, which is a painful disease of the spinal joints, have also been treated with large X-ray doses. The statistics in all these cases lead to the same conclusion: that large doses of radiation increase the likelihood that an individual's life will be shortened by leukemia and possibly also other cancers. Furthermore, it appears (mainly from the experiments on animals) that the increased likelihood is simply proportional to the amount of radiation received, at least for doses in the neighborhood of several hundred roentgens or so.

This of course sounds frightening. But the radiation doses from the world-wide fallout are in a completely different class from those we have been discussing. They are very much smaller. On the average human bones are getting about 0.002 roentgens per year from the Sr^{90} in the fallout. In addition the whole body is receiving a roughly equal amount in gamma rays, mainly from Cs^{137}. These figures apply to new bone in young children who have grown up in an environment of Sr^{90} in the northern part of the United States. This is a region of maximum fallout. Adults whose bones were made for the most part before the atomic testing started are getting about 0.0003 roentgens per year from Sr^{90}. None of these figures appears to be alarming.

At this present rate a lifetime dosage in northern U.S. is only a small fraction of a roentgen. A rare individual might get several times this amount. If tests continue at the present rate, radiation levels could increase by as much as five-fold. However, even in this situation it is difficult to imagine anyone receiving a lifetime dose of more than five or ten roentgens from the world-wide fallout. A more reasonable estimate for the average lifetime dose would be a few roentgens or less.

One might conclude from these figures that there is no danger whatsoever from the fallout. This conclusion, however, may not be correct.

The danger from such small doses of radiation is not easy to define. Even the best statistical methods are insufficient. One is looking for small effects which show up only after millions of cases have been studied. Animal experiments are extremely difficult to carry out under these conditions. Direct controlled experience with human beings is, of course, impossible. As a result, one is forced to draw conclusions from the effects at higher dose levels, where experimental data have been obtained.

This may be done in many ways. One way is to assume that the law of proportionality holds down to the smallest doses. This means that one roentgen produces one hundredth as many cases of bone cancer and leukemia as 100 roentgens produce. This law is plausible. It is by no means proven.

By arguing in this way one finds that for each megaton of fission energy which escapes from the test site in the world-wide fallout the lives of approximately four hundred persons would be shortened by leukemia or bone cancer. Under present conditions of testing, roughly one half of the fission products are deposited as close-in fallout in and near the test site. Per megaton of fission energy exploded, therefore, perhaps 200 persons may get leukemia or bone cancer. This figure could actually be higher, possibly even a thousand persons or more per megaton. It could also be lower. It could be zero.

It is possible that radiation of less than a certain intensity does not cause bone cancer or leukemia at all. In the past small doses of radiation have often been regarded as beneficial. This was not supported by any scientific evidence. Today many well-informed people believe that radiation is harmful even in the smallest amounts. This statement has been repeated in an authoritative manner. Actually there can be little doubt that radiation hurts the individual cell. But a living being is a most complex thing. Damage to a small fraction of the cells might be beneficial to the whole organism.

Some experiments on mice seem to show that exposure to a little radiation increases the life expectancy of the animals. Scientific truth is firm—when it is complete. The evidence of what a little radiation will do to a complex animal like a human being is in an early and uncertain state.

In any event the number of additional cases of leukemia and bone cancer due to the fallout radiation is certainly too small to be noticed against the natural incidence of these disorders.

In the next thirty years about 6,000,000 people throughout the world will die from leukemia and bone cancer. From past tests, which have involved the explosion of about fifty megatons of fission energy, the possibility exists that another 50×200, i.e., 10,000 cases may occur. Statistical methods are not able to find the difference between 6,000,000 and 6,010,000. There is no way to differentiate between the fallout-induced cases of leukemia and bone cancer, and those which occur naturally.

The possible shortening of ten thousand lives may seem rather ominous. But mere figures can be misleading. A better way to appreciate the danger from fallout is to compare it with other more familiar dangers. Such a comparison can be made with the natural background of cosmic rays and radioactivity in the earth and in our own bodies.

We are constantly and inescapably exposed to this radiation. Our ancestors have been exposed to it. The human race has evolved in such a radioactive environment. Moreover, the biological effects from different kinds of radiation can be compared in a meaningful way in terms of roentgens. Therefore the danger from Sr^{90} is not unknown in every respect. In some ways it is very well-known because we and all living beings have spent our days in a similarly dangerous surrounding. We live on an earth which has radioactivity in its rocks, which carries a similar activity in its waters, and which is exposed from all sides, to a rain of particles which produce effects identical with the effects of radioactive materials.

Not all radiations which have the same intensity (the same number of roentgens) have precisely the same effect. The damage produced also depends somewhat on the spacing of the ionized and disrupted molecules. The cosmic rays and the Sr^{90}, however, are quite similar even in this respect.

The reader will recall that the spacing of the ionization depends only on the charge and the speed of the ionizing particle. The ionizing particle from the Sr^{90} is an energetic beta ray, which has a charge of one and a speed close to that of light. A large part of the background radiation which reaches our bones comes from the cosmic rays. The main portion of the cosmic rays is due to the mesons. The meson, like the beta ray, has a unit charge and a speed close to that of light. The two particles may therefore be expected to produce identical biological effects. The only difference between their effects is that the beta ray does not have enough energy to leave the bones, while the meson is so energetic that it deposits its energy both in our bones and throughout our whole body. Thus if we compare a Sr^{90} dose with the same dose of cosmic rays the same effect to the bones must be expected. But the cosmic rays give rise to additional effects in our bodies.

The total background dose to the bones is about 0.15 roentgens per year for the average person living at sea level in the United States. Of this amount, about 0.035 roentgens is due to cosmic rays. At higher altitudes the cosmic ray dosage increases. In Denver, at an altitude of 5000 feet, the cosmic rays contribute 0.05 roentgens per year.

The above numbers should be compared with the present level of world-wide fallout radiation to the bones: about 0.003 roentgens per year (from Sr^{90} and other sources). The fallout radiation is thus only a few per cent of the natural cosmic radiation. It is small even when compared to the variation of cosmic ray intensity between sea level and 5000 feet.

A correlation between the frequency of leukemia and bone cancer, and the intensity of natural radiation has been looked for. Some statistics for the year 1947, before weapons testing began, are available. They show the number of cases of these diseases occurring in that year per 100,000 population.

	Bone Cancer	Leukemia
Denver	2.4	6.4
New Orleans	2.8	6.9
San Francisco	2.9	10.3

The extra radiation that one gets in Denver from cosmic rays is many times greater than the fallout radiation. But the table shows no increased incidence of bone cancer or leukemia. On the contrary—the incidence of these diseases is actually lower in Denver.

Not all of the natural background radiation is due to cosmic rays. Part of the background comes from natural radioactive elements in the soil and in the drinking water. These include uranium, potassium[40], thorium and radium. Radium behaves like calcium and strontium, and gets deposited in our bones. All these effects are, to the best of our knowledge, at least as intensive in the Denver area as in San Francisco or New Orleans.

One possible explanation for the lower incidence of bone cancer and leukemia in Denver is that disruptive processes like radiation are not necessarily harmful in small enough doses. Cell deterioration and regrowth go on all the time in living creatures. A slight acceleration of these processes could conceivably be beneficial to the organism. One should not forget that while radiation can cause cancer, it has been used in massive doses to retard and sometimes even to cure cancer. The reason is that some cancer cells are more strongly damaged by radiation than the normal cells.

In spite of the table, however, there may actually be an increased tendency toward bone cancer and leukemia that results from living in Denver. If so—and this is the main point—the effect is too small to be noticed compared to other effects. We must remember that Denver differs from New Orleans and San Francisco in many ways (besides altitude), and these differences may also influence the statistics.

A more thorough consideration of the background radiation gives further evidence that this radiation is more important than the present or expected effects of Sr^{90}. The radium deposited in our bones from drinking water has been observed to reach values as high as 0.55 roentgens per year. Furthermore the heavier and slower alpha particles emitted by radium cause ionization processes which occur in closer spacing and are therefore more damaging than the ionization due to Sr^{90}. To make things worse radium is deposited in our bones in little nodules (hot spots). Thus the possibility of local damage is enhanced.

The background radiation to which we are exposed varies for some unexpected reasons. It has been pointed out recently that brick may contain more natural radioactivity than wood. The difference between living in a brick house and living in a wood house could give rise to ten times as much radiation as we are currently getting from fallout. (The additional radiation from the brick might be as much as 0.03 roentgens per year.)

Human beings are subject to radiation not only from natural sources, but also from man-made sources. One of these is wearing a wrist watch with a luminous dial. Another is having X-rays for medical purposes. Both of these sources give much more radiation than the fallout.

Of all ionizing radiation to which we are exposed the X-rays are most important. In some cases medical X-rays have intensities which are noticeably harmful. Yet this damage is practically always of little consequence compared to the advantage from correct recognition of any trouble that the X-ray discloses.

We may summarize in this way. Our knowledge of the effects from the fallout is deficient. We cannot say exactly how many lives may be impaired or shortened. On the other hand, our knowledge is sufficient to state that the fallout effect is below the statistically observable limit. It is also considerably less than the effect produced by moving from sea level to an elevated location like Denver, where cosmic radiation has a greater intensity. It is also less than having a chest X-ray every year. In other words, we know enough to state positively that the danger from the world-wide fallout is less than many other radiation effects which have not worried people and do not worry them now.

We have compared radiation from the fallout with radiation from other sources. It is also possible and helpful to compare the fallout danger with different kinds of dangers. For this purpose it is convenient to express all dangers in terms of a reduced life-expectancy. For example, smoking one pack of cigarettes a day seems to cut one's life-expectancy by about 9 years. This is equivalent to 15 minutes per cigarette. That cigarettes are this harmful is, of course, not known with certainty. It is a "best guess," due to Dr. Hardin Jones, based on an analysis of statistical data. A number of Dr. Jones' statistical findings are listed in the following table:[1]

	Reduced Life Expectancy
Being 10 per cent overweight	1.5 years
Smoking one pack of cigarettes a day	9 years
Living in the city instead of the country	5 years
Remaining unmarried	5 years
Having a sedentary job instead of one involving exercise	5 years
Being of the male sex	3 years
Automobile accidents	1 year
One roentgen of radiation	5 to 10 days
The world-wide fallout (lifetime dose at present level)	1 to 2 days

The reader will see that the world-wide fallout is as danger-ous as being an ounce overweight or smoking one cigarette every two months.

[1] The last line of the table is based on our own estimates.

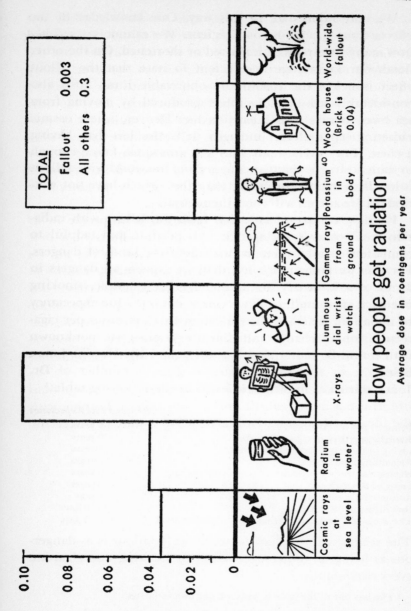

How people get radiation

Average dose in roentgens per year

TOTAL
Fallout   0.003
All others 0.3

The objection may be raised that the fallout, while not yet dangerous, may become so as more nations develop and test atomic weapons. On this point we can only say that the future is not easy to predict. Some factors, however, justify optimism. We are learning how to regulate the fallout by exploding bombs under proper surroundings. Development of clean bombs will greatly reduce the radioactivity produced. Deep underground tests will eliminate fallout altogether. The activity put into the atmosphere in 1954 was considerably greater than the activity released in any other year. It is highly probable that the activity produced by United States tests will continue to decline.

Finally, we may remark that radiation is unspecific in its effects. Chemicals are specific. About the effects of a new ingredient in our diet, in our medicine, or in the air we breathe, we know much less than we know about radiation. If we should worry about our ignorance concerning our chemical surroundings as we worry about the possible effects of radiation, we would be condemned to a conservatism that would stop all change and stifle all progress. Such conservatism would be more immobile than the empire of the Pharaohs.

It has been claimed that it is wrong to endanger any human life. Is it not more realistic and in fact more in keeping with the ideals of humanitarianism to strive toward a better life for all mankind?

CHAPTER XIII

Danger to the Race

R̲ADIATION MAY hurt the individual. It may also
be harmful for our children and hurt the race. We have seen
that the danger from the radiation due to testing is small
compared to many risks which we habitually take and almost
always ignore, which in fact we have to ignore to continue to
live in this civilized world. In addition we are not even quite
sure that the danger to the individual is real.

There can be little doubt, however, that radiation does
produce some harmful changes in our children. What seems
even more frightening, is that these changes may not show
up in our children but only in their children or further
progeny. A danger which may lie hidden for generations
might seem more terrifying, especially as it has often been
repeated that all such radiation effects are harmful.

We transmit our properties to coming generations in a
most curious and concentrated fashion. From the mother and
the father a child inherits a number of chromosomes, twenty-
four from each.[1] These are structures along which the actual
carriers of the properties—the genes—are strung up.

[1] Recent evidence suggests this number is sometimes twenty-three.

We are beginning to understand something about the nature of the genes. They seem to be very big spiral molecules. They carry the master plan of our body and even of our character in a strange chemical code.

The laws of heredity are complicated because of the fact that the same property is influenced by a gene from each parent. Frequently these two genes dictate different behavior and then the result is a compromise, sometimes evenhanded, sometimes unbalanced. But of the two genes only one will find its way to the child of the next generation. The compromise is temporary and original properties may emerge again. Which one of any pair of chromosomes (or of the two assemblies of genes) carries on is a matter of chance. In the world of the cells as in the world of atoms it is chance that determines the future—not fate.

Of all these facts we need be particularly interested in one. The units of inheritance are rather constant but not quite immutable. There is a small possibility that any gene may suffer a mutation. That is, it may turn into a new chemical, carrying a new code and new properties.

A gene is an extremely finely and precisely constituted object. It must be so in order to carry all the racial past in so little material. A mutation due to chance will spoil this order in almost every instance. The great majority of mutations are detrimental. Many are lethal.

It is an incredible fact that these random mutations, almost always harmful and never proceeding according to any plan, should have been responsible in the very long run for all the many beautiful and perfect living creatures that nature has produced (and this includes the human race). The thread leading from single cells to cell colonies, worms, fishes, vertebrates, mammals and human beings does certainly not seem to be the work of chance. Much less does it seem to be the work of a gamble taking one chance of a small improvement against a thousand chances of deformity or death. Nevertheless it is such a terrible game of chance which has produced both the human body and in some manner also the human spirit.

Big numbers are strange things and when each member of a huge assembly must be given individual attention then the numbers are even harder to appreciate. Billions of contemporary lives in billions of distinct generations have led to the incredible outcome: the harmony of life produced by gambling.

Radiation is surely disruptive. It does cause mutations. Since the genes appear to be single molecules, a single process of ionization or excitation is likely to result in a change. As has been said before there is doubt whether or not cancer and leukemia can be caused by exceedingly little radiation. There is little doubt, however, that mutations can be caused by any small amount of radiation. The less radiation the less the chance. But the chance will always be there.

A very great increase in the natural rate of mutations could indeed have terrifying effects. We can be quite certain, however, that radiation from atomic tests will increase the chance of mutations by only a very small amount.

The argument is essentially the same as the one concerning the danger to the individual. The tests are responsible for 0.001 or 0.002 roentgens per year to the human reproductive cells. This is equivalent to approximately 0.05 roentgen per generation. Most of this radiation is due to gamma rays from Cs^{137} which has been deposited on the ground or absorbed in the body. The number of mutations caused by this radiation is to be compared with the number of natural mutations.

Some of the natural mutations are caused by heat and chemicals. Some are due to background radiation, to cosmic rays or to gamma and beta rays emitted by natural radioactive substances in or near our bodies. Our best estimate is that 10 per cent of the natural mutations are due to the background radiation.

Over a period of one generation the background radiation dosage to the human reproductive cells is approximately five roentgens. Assuming a simple proportionality between dosage and the number of mutations, it follows that fifty roentgens would be required to induce a number of mutations equal to the total number of natural mutations (from background radiation and all other causes). That is, fifty roentgens is a "doubling dose."

The atomic tests are therefore increasing the number of mutations by about $0.05 \div 50$, which is 0.1 per cent. This kind of increase in the rate of mutations would certainly not seem to be a serious reason for worry.

Actually the number of mutations from the tests is very small even compared to geographical and altitude variations in the natural radioactivity. The Inca empire existed for many generations in the high country of Peru. The people of Tibet have been exposed for generation after generation to the greater cosmic ray intensity which bombards them through a thinner layer of atmosphere. These people have been exposed to much greater additional radiation than anything which is caused by atomic tests. Yet genetic differences have not been noticed in the human race or for that matter in any other living species in Peru or Tibet. We are certainly talking here about questions which may strike hard on some individuals but which from the point of view of the community or race are not serious.

It has been often repeated that all mutations due to radiation are harmful. There is every reason to believe that mutations due to radiation are not different in kind from other mutations. Should we then seriously believe that all mutations are harmful? That most of them are is admitted. If all of them were indeed always harmful, we must deny the simplest facts of evolution.

There will be some who maintain that the human race is not capable of improvement. Such an argument is irrefutable. It is also unreasonable. What cannot be further improved is perfect, and not many people will maintain that our species can claim perfection.

Another and much more plausible argument has been advanced: In the wild state living species do perfect themselves by means of natural selection. Human society by caring for the imperfect and defective individual has eliminated natural selection. Therefore further mutations will not improve mankind.

It is very hard to discuss this question for the simple reason that the argument involves the interaction of two processes extremely different in magnitude and in fact different in kind. On the one hand it concerns itself with evolution which proceeds in the slow deliberate way of a glacier. On the other hand it focuses attention upon the process of human civilization with its technical and social changes which has gained momentum like an avalanche. The momentum is still there and it is still increasing and where we shall land we do not know. To consider the motion of the glacier while being carried along by the avalanche puts things completely out of proportion. Long before the present rates of mutation could have any effect upon the human species we shall live in a very different world and we shall have started to influence our own behavior including those of selection, natural or otherwise, in ways which today we cannot foresee.

If we discuss the question how civilization will influence natural selection, we shall not do it with the hope of arriving at a firm answer. We shall do it rather in order to illustrate how doubtful all the arguments are which concern the interplay of two processes which cannot be measured in the same scale.

It is true that we can and do preserve the lives of children who, because of inherited weaknesses, would perish under natural conditions. It is true too that we do this for reasons and for feelings concerning the individual and we do it without regard to the consequences to the race. However, under our present condition of civilization a disease which can be corrected by administering chemicals or using the surgeon's knife is no longer effectively a disease. In our present condition such a life can be as valuable to society and to the race as a life which does not have these superficial shortcomings. That we can and do preserve more life in this manner only emphasizes that under present conditions biological differences which used to be important no longer matter.

On the other hand, in social living many properties which used to be indifferent for a wild being have become of great significance. Ability to communicate and to get along with our fellows is not the only one, but is perhaps the most obvious one of such properties. The struggle for existence has become more gentle, and the chance of any individual to live on in his children is governed by new ways of behavior. Nevertheless the difference between the individual adapted to civilized living and the one who is not adapted is of great importance and will become of greater importance. It is likely that civilization will not eliminate evolution of the race. Rather it will direct it into new paths.

But the greatest change might be expected from an entirely different direction. We are going to understand in real detail the intricacies of human inheritance. Then we shall be faced with problems and shall find possibilities of an entirely new and different kind. The interest of a person in his children is not a superficial one. It is one of the most strong and lasting forces in biology, sociology and history. A clear understanding of the details of inheritance may bring about some grave difficulties because a new situation is never fitted easily into existing patterns of living. In the end more understanding may bring about improvements of a kind beside which all the worthwhile things that have been so far accomplished, might look unimportant.

The real importance of radioactivity for heredity does not

lie in the fact that we may speed up the glacier by one inch in a millennium. The real importance of nuclear radiation is rather that it is helping us to understand the strange processes of life and the curious substances which connect one generation to the next.

CHAPTER XIV

The Cobalt Bomb

NUCLEAR EXPLOSIONS seem horrible for many reasons. They were presented to an unprepared world as a dramatic surprise—as the climax to the slaughter of the Second World War. Their power of destruction is fantastic. Before we had adjusted our thinking to atomic bombs, an even more potent tool of warfare—the hydrogen bomb—was invented. Worst of all: To the fear of destruction there was added the dread of the unknown. It is not surprising that discussion of nuclear weapons has not proceeded on a purely rational level.

To the nightmare of the atomic and hydrogen bombs has been added—not as a reality but as a further threat—the cobalt bomb. The idea of such a bomb is to intensify the most terrifying aspect of nuclear explosions: the radioactivity. This radioactivity could be used to poison the enemy. It could get out of hand and poison everyone.

Cobalt[60] is a radioactive isotope of the fairly common metal cobalt. It can be easily produced by absorbing slow neutrons in the natural and stable cobalt[59]. It has a half-life of five years and it emits penetrating gamma rays. These properties make it useful in cancer therapy.

Many cancerous growths are more sensitive to radiation than healthy tissue. Therefore radiation can be used to reduce—sometimes even to destroy—dangerous tumors. The penetrating rays of cobalt[60] can reach the cancer even deep inside the human body. The lifetime of cobalt[60] is long enough so that this substance is easily installed in hospitals.

But the same properties which make cobalt[60] useful also make it potentially dangerous. A nuclear explosion produces many neutrons and these could be absorbed in ordinary cobalt. The radioactivity produced in this way lives long enough to become widely distributed. Its ray can easily penetrate a foot of masonry and several hundred feet of air. A cobalt bomb would indeed be a most unpleasant object. (See pictures 7 and 8.)

One widely discussed possibility is that future nuclear tests will be used to develop a cobalt bomb or other bombs for radiological warfare. Actually tests have little to do with the cobalt bomb. Once one has a powerful nuclear weapon, such as a hydrogen bomb, it is relatively easy to make a radiological bomb. Further tests are not necessarily required. To the extent that any testing need be carried out, it is only necessary to activate a moderate amount of substance to find out in what way a certain bomb would function as a tool of radiological warfare. Tests of this kind would add only a negligible amount of radioactivity to the atmosphere. Therefore, in connection with the test program we need not worry about the cobalt bomb or any related experiment. The question of the cobalt bomb or radiological warfare in general is not whether it is feasible—it is—but rather whether it serves a useful military purpose.

It is not impossible that situations might arise in which radiological warfare could be militarily advantageous. Instead of cobalt, other materials may be placed near the nuclear bombs. In this way other radioactive substances can be produced. By an appropriate choice of such a substance one can get a radioactive material which, when deposited near the point of explosion, will contaminate the site for a time which can be adjusted to the military requirements. The lifetime of the radioactive material may be long enough to give an opportunity to the people to escape from the contaminated area. At the same time, one may precipitate almost all the activity near the explosion so that distant localities would not be seriously affected. It is conceivable, therefore, that radiological warfare could be used in a humane manner. By exploding a weapon of this kind near an island one might be able to force evacuation without loss of human life. No instrument, not even a weapon, is evil in itself. Everything depends on the way in which it is used.

Public opinion has all but persuaded itself that nuclear weapons will be used not for a military objective but to terrorize and kill the greatest number of people. This is technically feasible. In fact, it does not even require the atomic bomb. For the last hundred years this possibility has been with us. Bacteriological warfare may cause widespread destruction. Yet no one has resorted to this horrible way of making war. We do not believe that anyone will expose his enemy and ultimately himself to indiscriminate bacteriological or radiological destruction. Our guarantee against this danger is not that it cannot be done. Our guarantee is the better and saner part of human nature: the will to survive and the feeling of common decency.

CHAPTER XV

What About Future Tests?

MANY PEOPLE feel that tests should be discontinued. This feeling is widespread and strong. The question of tests is obviously important. It may influence our security as individuals. It certainly will influence our security as a nation. If in a free, democratic country the majority believes that something should be done—it will be done. The sovereign power in a democracy is "the people." It is of the greatest importance that the people should be honestly and completely informed about all relevant facts. In no other way can a sound decision be reached. The basic and relevant facts are simple. The story can be presented without unnecessary frills or undue emotion. When this has been done, the right decision will be reached by common sense rather than by exceptional cleverness.

Unfortunately much of the discussion about continued experimentation with nuclear explosives has been carried out in a most emotional and confused manner. One argument concerning tests is so fantastic that it deserves to be mentioned for that very reason: It has been claimed that nuclear explosions may change the axis of the earth.

Of course, nuclear explosions do produce such changes. Only the changes are so small that they are impossible to observe and even difficult to estimate. Searching for effects connected with past tests that may displace the axis of the earth, or the position of the North Pole, we could find no effect that would have caused a change of position even as great as the size of an atom. One could design tests with the specific purpose to produce such a change, but these man-made effects could not be compared even remotely with the forces of nature. The motion of the Gulf Stream has a small effect on the North Pole; but this effect is incomparably greater than what any nuclear explosion could accomplish. It is good to know that the old top on which we live does have some stability.

The argument about world-wide radioactive fallout is more serious. It is asserted that fallout is dangerous and that we are ignorant of the extent of the danger.

In a narrow, literal sense both these statements are correct. But in the preceding chapters we have seen that the danger is limited. We do not know precisely how great it is. We do know, however, that the danger is considerably smaller than the danger from other radiations to which we continue to expose ourselves without worry. The danger from the tests is quite small compared with the effects of X-rays used in medical practice. The fallout produces only a fraction of the increase in cosmic ray effect to which a person subjects himself when he moves from the seashore to a place of higher altitude like Colorado. People may or may not be damaged by the fallout. But it is quite certain that the damage is far below a level of which we usually take notice.

Fallout in the vicinity of the test sites did cause damage. In the past this damage was not great although in one Pacific test it was serious. Precautions have been increased and we may hope that future accidents will be avoided altogether. The safety record of the Atomic Energy Commission compares favorably with other enterprises of similar scale.

It seems probable that the root of the opposition to further tests is not connected with fallout. The root is deeper. The real reason against further tests is connected with our desire for disarmament and for peace.

There can be no doubt that the desire for peace is most deep, and this desire is felt by all thinking and honest people on our earth. All of us certainly hope that the catastrophe of war can be avoided. This great and universal wish for peace is the driving force behind the desire for disarmament. In the minds of most people it would be an important step toward disarmament if the testing of nuclear weapons were stopped by all nations. This belief is widely held, but it is not necessarily well-founded. In fact, there are arguments on the other side which should be considered carefully.

It is generally believed that the First World War was caused by an arms race. For some strange reason most people forget that the Second World War was brought about by a situation which could be called a race in disarmament. The peace-loving and powerful nations divested themselves of their military power. When the Nazi regime in Germany adopted a program of rapid preparation for war, the rest of the world was caught unawares. At first they did not want to accept the fact of this menace. When the danger was unmistakable, it was too late to avert a most cruel war, and almost too late to stop Hitler short of world conquest. Unfortunately, disarmament is safe only when no one wants to impose his will by force of arms upon his neighbors.

In the uneasy world in which we live today no reasonable person will advocate unilateral disarmament. What people hope is that all sides will agree to reduce their military power and thereby contribute to a more peaceful atmosphere. The elimination of tests has appeared possible and proper for two reasons. One is that tests are conspicuous, and therefore it is believed that we can check whether or not testing has actually been stopped by everyone. The second reason is that nuclear explosives already represent such terrifying power that further tests appear useless and irrational. These arguments are simple and almost universally accepted. They are based on misconceptions.

A nuclear explosion is a violent event, but in the great expanses of our globe such tests can be effectively hidden if appropriate care is taken to hide them. There can be no doubt that this is possible. The question is only how much it costs to hide a test and how big is the explosion that can be carried out in secret for a certain amount of expenditure.

If an agreement were made to discontinue the tests, the United States would surely keep such an agreement. The very social and political structure of our country excludes the possibility that many people would collaborate in breaking an international undertaking. Whether Russia would or would not keep such an agreement would depend on the ingenuity of the Russians, on their willingness to make economic sacrifices, and on their honesty. Of these three factors we can have a firm opinion about the first. The Russians are certainly ingenious enough to devise secret methods of testing. As to the other questions, whether the Russians will want to invest the effort and whether they will be bound by their word, we feel that each man is entitled to his own opinion. According to past experience, an agreement to stop tests may well be followed by secret and successful tests behind the iron curtain.

In a more general way we may ask the question: Is it wise to make agreements which honesty will respect, but dishonesty can circumvent? Shall we put a free, democratic government at a disadvantage compared to the absolute power of a dictatorship? Shall we introduce prohibition in a new form, just to give rise to bootlegging on a much greater scale? It is almost certain that in the competition between prohibition and bootlegging, the bootlegger will win.

All of these arguments, however, would become irrelevant if it were true that further testing would not accomplish any further desirable result. It has been said and often repeated that we now possess adequate nuclear explosives to wipe out the cities of any enemy. What more do we need?

Our main purpose in further experimentation with nuclear bombs is not, of course, to make city-busters more horrible. We would prefer not to have to use our nuclear weapons at all. We keep them as a counterthreat against the danger that we ourselves should be subjected to a devastating attack. To understand what we are actually trying to do in the tests, we have to take a closer look at some military problems.

In the Second World War strategic bombing was used for the first time on a really massive scale. It may well be and, in fact, it is probable that such strategic bombing will not be repeated in the future.

There are two military reasons for the bombing of cities. One is that factories are located in cities, and these factories support the war effort. The other reason is that cities are centers of transportation through which the supplies of war materials pass. By destroying these centers the flow of the war supplies can be interrupted.

Nuclear warfare is likely to be quite different from past conflicts. The great concentration of firepower which a nuclear weapon represents makes it possible to attack on enemy anywhere, at very short notice. This is true no matter what the particular target is, whether one is trying to attack the planes, ships, tanks, or troop concentrations of an enemy. The great mobility of nuclear firepower makes it highly probable that the nuclear conflict will be short. What the factory produces during this conflict will not affect the outcome of the fighting. The only weapons on which anyone can rely are the weapons which are already stockpiled. Therefore, it will be militarily useless to bomb factories.

The same fact of mobility also implies that no great flow of war material will need to be maintained. Practically all movement can be executed by light and fast methods, by planes, submarines, and small battle groups. Under these conditions the cities will lose their importance as centers of transportation.

The only purpose in bombing cities will be to spread terror among the enemy. This was rarely done in past wars. In fact, terror is self-defeating because it provokes retaliation from the other side.

We believe that the role of nuclear weapons in a future war is by no means the killing of millions of civilians. It is rather to stop the armed forces of an aggressor. This is not easy to do because it requires not only nuclear weapons, but very special kinds of nuclear weapons which are hard to develop and harder to perfect. But with proper experimentation and proper planning the defensive use of nuclear weapons is possible.

The idea of tactical nuclear weapons is not new. The possibility of using nuclear explosives in small wars has been frequently discussed. What kind of weapons do we need in order to fight these small wars and to defend the freedom of people wherever such defense becomes necessary? It has often been suggested that in small wars, small weapons will be used, while big weapons are appropriate for big wars. Such a statement is much too simple and has no relation to reality. In every case the right kind of weapon is the one which performs the job of stopping the enemy's armed forces without inflicting unnecessary loss on the innocent bystander. For this purpose we need a great number of weapons which are adaptable to specific purposes, which are easy to transport and easy to deliver, and give rise to the kind of effect which the situation requires.

For instance, a nuclear weapon may be carried by a fighter plane and used to shoot down an attacking bomber. Since the carrying capacity of the fighter plane is severely limited, the weapon for this purpose must be small and light. A major objective of the test program is to develop such purely defensive weapons.

The encounter between the fighter plane and the bomber may well take place in our own country over populated areas. This possibility would fill most people with alarm lest the population underneath the explosion should be hurt. Fortunately, in a recent nuclear test in Nevada, five well-informed and courageous Air Force officers demonstrated that there is complete safety to people on the ground. They did this by standing directly beneath the explosion at ground zero.

This important test took place only a few months ago— on July 19, 1957. An F-89 jet fighter plane flying at 19,000 feet above sea level delivered an air-to-air atomic rocket to a preassigned point in the sky. The ground zero men were 15,000 feet immediately below. They wore no helmets, no sun-glasses, and no protective clothing.

At the instant of the explosion the men looked up, saw the fireball and felt the heat. There was no discomfort, only a gentle warmth. Then they waited for the shock wave to arrive—approximately ten seconds. When the shock came, it was actually just a loud noise. However, one of the men ducked his head instinctively. (See pictures 9 and 10.)

The blast and the thermal pulse were over. But the Air Force men stood their ground. One question still remained: Would there be any fallout? They checked their radiation instruments and waited while the cloud drifted slowly away. There was no significant rise in the radiation level. The test had been a complete success. The effects of the explosion were utterly insignificant on the ground. But high in the air an enemy plane could have been demolished even if the nuclear explosion had missed it by a considerable distance.

In order that nuclear weapons should be effective against armed invaders, it is clear that great numbers of these weapons are needed. Such great numbers of weapons, some of which must be ground-burst, will produce a considerable amount of radioactive contamination, and this contamination will endanger friend and foe alike. In particular, the radioactivity is likely to kill people in the very country whose liberty we are trying to defend. For this reason it is most important that we should be able to use nuclear weapons which cause the least possible contamination. In recent nuclear tests more and more attention has been paid to the development of such clean weapons, and most fortunately these efforts are well on the way toward success.

The radioactive fallout from nuclear testing gives rise to a possible danger which is quite limited in size. The danger from the fallout in a nuclear war, however, would be real and great. If we stop testing now, and if we should fail to develop to the fullest possible extent these clean weapons, we should unnecessarily kill a great number of noncombatants. Not to develop the explosives with the smallest radioactive fallout would, indeed, be completely inexcusable.

The only alternative is that nuclear weapons should not be used at all. Since these weapons have been presented as purely evil instruments, most people hope that they will never be used, and indeed one should hope that wars, and therefore the use of these weapons, can be avoided.

But in our conflict with the powerful communistic countries which strive for world domination, it may be too much to hope for uninterrupted peace. If we abandon our light and mobile weapons, we shall enable the Red bloc to take over one country after another, close to their borders, as opportunities arise. The free nations cannot maintain the massive armies throughout the world which would be required to resist such piecemeal aggression. On the other hand, the flexible power of clean nuclear explosives would put us in a position where we could resist aggression in any part of the world, practically at a moment's notice.

The announced policy of our country is to maintain peace and stability in the world. By being patient and prepared we are trying to arrive at a world order based on law and justice for all peoples. There is no doubt that this policy is supported by the overwhelming majority of Americans. Our armed forces need the greatest possible flexibility in order to give strength to this policy. Such flexibility we can possess only if we have in our possession the strongest, best developed weapons which are also the cleanest, so that they may be used for defense rather than for random destruction.

If we renounce nuclear weapons, we open the door to aggression. If we fail to develop clean explosives, we expose people to disaster from radioactive fallout in any serious military conflict. To our way of thinking these are weighty arguments in favor of continued experimentation and development of nuclear weapons. But still another, more general, point of view should be considered.

The spectacular developments of the last centuries, in science, in technology, and in our everyday life, have been based on one important premise: to explore fearlessly any consequences to which greater knowledge and improved skills can lead us. When we talk about nuclear tests, we have in mind not only military preparedness but also the execution of experiments which will give us more insight and more ability to control the forces of nature. There are many specific political and military reasons why such experiments should not be abandoned. There also exists this very general reason—the tradition of exploring the unknown. We can follow this tradition, and we can at the same time be increasingly careful that radioactivity, carelessly dispersed, should not interfere with human life.

CHAPTER XVI

Has Something Happened to the Weather?

THE WEATHER is no longer quite as unpredict-able as it used to be. Yet we are hardly ever sure of it even a few hours in advance. One week is about the limit of the period of any prediction. Where the best men lack knowl-edge untrammeled fantasy has a field day. Weather has so far remained a safe topic of conversation and of speculation.

Nuclear explosions have, of course, been made responsible for the weather—for any kind of unusual weather. Be it rain or drought or a hard season of hurricanes—the nuclear tests are dragged in. The weather bureau says: no. But then—the weather bureau has not always been correct. Indeed it would be a miracle if the popular talk and the popular press would not have seen some connection between atomic explosions and the wayward behavior of the seasons.

In one case—and to our knowledge only in one case— there has occurred a chain of events starting with a nuclear test and ending in a copious and unusual downpour. In the spring of 1955 a test shot of moderate size was fired in Nevada. At the same time the last storm of the season was blowing it-self out in California. According to the usual rules of meteorology the radioactive cloud should have been carried east by the steady westerly winds which blow over the temperate zone. But this time the cloud was caught up by the swirl of the dying California storm and some of the radioactivity was carried to the west coast.

Hours after the explosion radioactive rain began to fall in California. The activity was weak enough and did not give rise to any worry. But a remarkable thing happened. As the active cloud arrived over California the storm revived. It developed into an abundant rain which is not usual at that place and time. Did we—quite unintentionally—do something about the weather?

The weather bureau said: no. One must certainly admit that this single case proves nothing. Only greatly improved methods of weather observation and weather prediction would make it possible to decide if such a chain of events consists of the strong links of cause and effect or else of a simple sequence of haphazard occurrences.

Even though our knowledge is incomplete there is at least one simple fact which should be borne in mind. All the energy in that Nevada explosion was not quite sufficient to evaporate the water droplets in a cloud one mile broad, one mile wide, and one mile deep. This is not a very big rain cloud. Such a cloud would give about one third of an inch of rain water over one square mile—not an impressive amount. Even the biggest hydrogen bomb would give only energy enough to evaporate a cloud ten miles by ten miles and towering to the top of the "boiling" portion of our air, which we call the troposphere. This would give roughly three inches of rain over a hundred square miles—a more impressive amount but vanishing in the vastness of the Pacific Ocean.

Nuclear explosions are violent enough. But compared to the forces of nature—compared even with the daily release of energy from not particularly stormy weather—all our bombs are puny. Offhand one might guess that our nuclear fireworks could not swing the scales in the massive energy changes that we see around us in the common occurrences of wind and rain.

But the interplay of clouds and sunshine, of water evaporating, freezing, dropping and thawing—in short the vagaries of weather—are both involved and tricky. Small causes can give rise to big effects. Some processes of air masses sweeping over oceans and continents are irresistible and predictable. Others, like the first upsurge of hot air from the overheated ground, may be a question of close competition and trigger action. This is what makes it so difficult to predict the weather.

One of the most delicate processes we must think about is the formation of water droplets. When some water molecules are mixed with air molecules, we have moist air. If such air rises, expands and cools, the water molecules lose some of their agitated motion and have a greater tendency to stick together to form droplets. But it is not easy to get them started on this joint enterprise.

If two or three molecules stick together, they soon are shaken apart. If, however, two or three dozen are collected, this is enough to start a growth which ends in a droplet of water. If moist air is cooled, droplets will form, provided there is a meeting place from which the growth can start. If there is no such meeting place, there are no droplets and we get no cloud. If there are few meeting places, each will collect a rather great amount of water, we will get big drops, and we may get rain. If there is an abundance of meeting places many tiny droplets are formed which will remain suspended as a cloud. The present attempts at rain-making are connected with a birth-control of droplets.

We have seen earlier that in each radioactive decay charged particles are emitted. As these move along their paths, they tear up more atoms and leave in their wake an assembly of charged particles. These charged particles strongly attract the molecules of water. They attract the molecules of air much less. The reason is that in a water molecule positive and negative charges are separated to a considerable extent whereas in the nitrogen and oxygen molecules of air the charges are distributed more evenly. As a result the track of each particle emitted in a radioactive decay provides many meeting places for the formation of water droplets.

Actually, cooled moist air has been used for many decades to make the tracks of fast charged particles visible. In one of the photographs you can see a picture of such "vapor trails." It is a photograph through an apparatus called the Wilson Cloud Chamber. The myriads of radioactive disintegrations in the debris of a nuclear explosion can give vapor trails which coalesce into a real cloud. In this way weather might be influenced. (See pictures 11 and 12.)

In spite of all this it remains highly probable that testing of nuclear explosions, as practiced at present, does not influence the weather. Radioactivity does furnish an opportunity for droplets to form. But other abundant sources are also available for droplet formation. Dust, smoke and many forms of air pollution will do the trick. Foam scattered from ocean waves evaporates and leaves a speck of salt behind. This particle of salt may be carried by the winds for many miles and may eventually become the germ around which a new drop will condense. The cosmic rays by which we are bombarded give rise to vapor trails similar to those produced by the radioactive decay products. Among the many processes of nature and the usual by-products of civilization the few atomic tests do not play an important role. This statement can stand, not as a certainty, but as a very good guess.

Among the many surprises that the future holds one may be closely connected with the weather. In the age of the airplane we are getting more and more information about the air masses around us. Air travel demands this information and also furnishes it. New techniques, such as radar, can detect the formation of a cloud and can measure the size of droplets at a great distance. In fact the information received is so plentiful that one may doubt whether we can properly understand it and utilize it.

Fortunately we no longer need to rely exclusively on our own brains. Human thought is a remarkable thing but it is slow. The modern computing machines, the "electronic brains," are simpletons as compared to the apparatus which each of us wears in his skull. But the electronic computers have one advantage: they are fast. Soon they will be a million times as fast as our mental processes. The expression "fast as thought" is dated—it is a contemporary of the horse-and-buggy.

The electronic machines can digest weather information as fast as it is received. Some progress has already been made. In a few years all weather predictions may be machine-made.

This need not mean that weather can be predicted with certainty or for a long time ahead. The trigger processes which, starting from an insignificant and unnoticed spot of turbulence, can grow into the dimensions of a cyclone will set a limit to any art of prediction.

But to the extent that weather cannot be predicted it may be influenced. If small causes may have big effects then even the puny means available to man may change the weather—provided we know how and where to apply the lever.

First we shall have to acquire a better understanding of the weather-science of meteorology. Then we shall have to look for the appropriate trigger mechanism. This may be a cloud of dust of the right kind—or else a chemical—or perhaps a great number of radioactive particles. In one way or another atomic explosions may be used as the trigger but the trigger will not be effective until and unless the rest of the machinery is understood.

Of course atomic explosions cannot be used in really significant numbers unless we learn how to avoid those radioactive by-products which are really dangerous. Fortunately the use of nuclear fusion, best known from the hydrogen bomb, makes it possible to regulate the kind of radioactivity one obtains. We may make only such kinds of activity which decay before they have a chance to get into the human body.

Experience has proved that to talk about weather is not dangerous. To do something about the weather will be more risky. Shall the weather become a ward of the government? Shall we have Republican Rainstorms and Democratic Droughts? In this way we shall certainly lose the last safe topic of conversation.

In the narrower confines of Europe where sovereign nation is a few hours from sovereign nation (as the wind blows) the situation will be much more serious. But even the whole planet may prove too small for fiercely conflicting interests when more knowing fingers are placed on more sensitive triggers.

To govern the weather can be most useful. It could give ample livelihood to all the people of the earth and to many more billions. Such endeavor is surely good and it would appear peaceful. But in this case as in many other cases knowledge will lead to power and power will lead to disaster if it is not tempered by wisdom.

Yet this knowledge or some similarly dangerous knowledge will come to us in our lifetimes. Nuclear explosions do not stand alone as a potential source of mischief.

CHAPTER XVII

Safety of Nuclear Reactors

At the beginning of the scientific and industrial revolution two old ambitions were found to be impossible dreams. One was the transmutation of elements, the other the machine of perpetual motion.

Modern nuclear physicists had to retract one of these statements: elements can be transmuted. But the product is expensive, for the time being much more expensive than gold.

The perpetual motion machine remains impossible in principle but the problem may be considered solved in practice. It can be proved, of course, that a machine can do useful work only if it burns up some fuel. But the price of fuel is quite often less than the cost to operate and maintain the machine.

Nuclear fuel even today is no more expensive than conventional fuel in many parts of the United States. Nuclear fuel is neither heavy nor bulky and can be therefore transported easily. In those parts of the world where ordinary fuel is expensive, nuclear energy will soon become of great importance. Furthermore, we shall learn to use most of the energy in uranium rather than just the part contained in its rare and valuable isotope, U^{235}.

One only has to add a neutron to common U^{238} to get radioactive U^{239}. In the course of time this decays into plutonium. This element can be used like U^{265}: It produces fission, a great amount of energy and enough neutrons to keep the process going. We shall also learn to extract energy from other nuclear fuels. Thorium acts like uranium, while deuterium can give energy by building up bigger nuclei rather than breaking them into smaller pieces. Therefore the source of energy will be universally available and quite inexpensive. This really means that we are as well off as though we had a machine of perpetual motion.

But, of course, all this does not mean that the machine will do its job free of charge. Even a perpetual motion machine would need servicing and maintenance. Unfortunately our nuclear machines need a lot of such servicing and therefore for the time being, nuclear energy is not the cheapest.

The main reason why a nuclear energy source, or a nuclear reactor is difficult and expensive to run is that the reactor after a short time of operation becomes strongly radioactive. Therefore it cannot be approached and it has to be handled by remote control. We can hardly expect that energy will be free like air or water. But when we learn how to handle inexpensively our nuclear machines, we shall be able to obtain energy for a reasonable price at any place on the earth. Sooner or later conventional fuel will become scarce. But nuclear energy will allow the industrial revolution to continue and to expand into every corner of the earth.

There can be little doubt that during the next decades nuclear reactors will greatly multiply and by the beginning of the next century they will be found everywhere. It is therefore of the greatest importance that these reactors should be operated safely. On the face of it, a nuclear reactor is a sluggish instrument which can be made to run itself. But the ease of operation is deceptive. (See picture 13.)

One need not fear that a nuclear reactor might explode

like an atomic bomb. Nuclear explosives are very carefully constructed so that they can release a lot of energy in a short time. Nuclear reactors on the other hand are put together so as to make it possible that energy will be released only at a moderate rate. Some reactors if improperly handled may explode, but the violence of the explosion cannot greatly exceed that of a similar weight of high explosive.

Nevertheless a reactor accident could become exceedingly dangerous. The reactor is charged with radioactive fission products and some other radioactive substances produced by neutron absorption. Any accident which will allow even a portion of these products to escape into the air will endanger people at a considerable distance in the downwind direction. One reason why reactors can be dangerous is that in protracted operation of the reactor, fission products which have longer lives accumulate. It is precisely these longer-lived products which are more dangerous because they have a better chance to find their way into the human body.

Reactors are now planned which will produce 300,000 kilowatts of electricity. If such a reactor operates for half a year and then explodes and releases its radioactive content into the atmosphere, its radioactivity will be comparable to that of a hydrogen bomb. In one important respect such an accident would be worse than a hydrogen explosion. The nuclear explosive lifts most of its radioactive products to a high altitude and the poisonous activity gets dispersed and diluted before it descends. The activity from a reactor on the other hand will remain close to the ground and might endanger the lives of the people in an area of hundreds of square miles. It will contaminate an even greater territory.

In the extensive operation of many reactors in the United States no one has yet been killed by the radioactivity. This has been due to extremely careful operation and also to good luck. We must be prepared that sooner or later accidents will occur. On the other hand we must try to take sufficient precautions to avoid the kind of catastrophic accident which we have mentioned above. With great care such accidents can indeed be avoided.

In thinking of all kinds of man-made machines we find some which move fast and seem dangerous like, for instance, airplanes; others which are stationary and apparently harmless, like the bath tub. Yet more accidents happen in bath tubs than in air travel. The most dangerous element in all operations is the human element. We ourselves constitute the greatest safety hazard. This is a situation no different in nuclear technology than in any other kind of technology. What is new in nuclear technology is that a reactor is usually very safe but may become extremely dangerous when something unexpected happens to it. Also we dare not use the method of trial and error. An error in the reactor business could exact a far heavier toll of lives than an error in the testing of H-bombs. We cannot wait to learn by experience; we must forestall accidents.

An especially difficult safety problem is connected with the use of reactors in small countries. A serious accident could endanger the lives of people in adjacent countries. Thus modern technology may force cooperation across national boundaries.

There is only one way to avoid traffic accidents and that is care exercised by everyone, particularly the drivers. Similarly reactor safety will depend on the people who operate the reactors. At the same time a lot of help can be obtained by careful construction and scrutiny of each new reactor.

One of the first acts of the Atomic Energy Commission was to establish a Committee for Reactor Safeguards. With the passing of years this committee had to take on more heavy responsibilities. At first it had to operate under secrecy. With the wider and more public use of reactors the safety considerations are becoming more available to the public. The question of safe operation of a machine cannot be separated from a thorough understanding of the working of the machine. We cannot attempt to give an adequate description of a reactor or of the safety rules. A few general statements have to suffice.

A working reactor is full of neutrons. In a small fraction of a second these neutrons produce fission and a new generation of neutrons comes into being. In slow reactors which contain lots of light elements like hydrogen or carbon, the neutrons move with speeds little greater than that of sound and a generation may last as long as a millisecond (one thousandth of a second). In fast reactors which contain almost exclusively heavier elements like uranium or iron, neutrons move with a great speed which is about three per cent of the speed of light. In this case one generation replaces another in less than a microsecond (one millionth of a second).

Fortunately not all the neutrons get reproduced so rapidly. Some fissions produce delayed neutrons which are emitted usually with a delay of several seconds. In a steadily working reactor each generation should have the same number of neutrons as the previous one. If each succeeding generation has even a slight surplus, the reactor will become hot and may explode in a small fraction of a second. The main reason why safe operation is possible is the fact that fast multiplication can occur only if each generation becomes more populous *even when one does not count the delayed neutrons.* A slightly overactive reactor is easily governed, but there comes a point when the dormant dragon begins to stir. This happens when there are enough neutrons produced so that multiplication can occur without waiting for the delayed neutrons. At that point a well behaved dragon will perform a harmless action. For instance it may blow a fuse. But a vicious dragon will spit radioactive fire.

It is not easy to predict whether the dragon will be always well behaved. But with careful analysis one can make such a prediction. For instance one must look into the question of whether the reactor is stable. If it gets hotter, does this make the reactor proceed even faster so that the rate of heating increases and the reactor runs away? In a stable reactor excess heat should tend to stop the energy production and thus the reactor cools and returns to its normal operating temperature.

But too great a stability may also be dangerous. Heating may be overcompensated by the cooling mechanism; after the reactor has become too cold it may then heat up too fast and overshoot again. We must guard not only against a simple run-away, but also against increasing oscillations.

In many reactors unusual chemical compounds are used. A reactor accident may start with nothing worse than an ordinary chemical reaction between strange compounds under strange conditions. But if this chemical reaction destroys the reactor sufficiently to allow some fission products to escape, then such a chemical accident can be as bad as one of nuclear origin.

In the interior of the reactor materials are exposed to unusually strong radiation. Under this effect some materials can change their chemical properties so that what has been inert as a construction material may become dangerous during the operation of the reactor.

Perhaps the most important single item is the arrangement of mechanical controls. The reactor is adjusted by a system of sheets or rods made of a material which absorbs neutrons. This arrangement must be so constructed that the control rods can be withdrawn only at a very slow rate. But it must be possible to put them back quite fast. Any danger signal should shove the absorbers in at maximum speed. The technical expression is "scram."

The main point, however, is that all the dangers and safety devices can be studied and after careful study a nuclear accident can be avoided. Some reactors are now so thoroughly understood that they can be safely used for training of future nuclear engineers. Other reactors which are more powerful or less well studied have to be used more carefully. Some reactors should be, and are being, enclosed in gas-tight containers. If an explosion occurs the fission products will be harmlessly confined inside the container. Of course, one must be quite sure that the reactor is of such a type that it cannot produce an explosion great enough to burst the container and what is even more important one should be quite sure that the container is closed except when the reactor is shut down and completely safe. Often it may be best to build the reactor underground.

The safety of a reactor, of course, depends to a great extent on the use to which the reactor is put. In general a power station is less likely to give trouble than a moving power source. It is not probable that nuclear locomotives will ever be safe. In nuclear ships more room is available and more room permits more safety measures. But even so the safety of nuclear motors in ships will have to be considered particularly carefully because ships will have accidents in harbors.

Between the urgent need for progress and the absolute necessity of safety it is difficult to keep a sense of balance and one can easily make the mistake of being unnecessarily cautious. Such unnecessary caution was probably exercised when the Committee on Reactor Safeguards considered the earthquake hazard of the Brookhaven reactor on Long Island. A seismologist, who is a Jesuit Father, was asked to tell the committee[1] of the possibilities and probabilities of an earthquake on Long Island. The chairman[2] of the committee subjected the expert to a long and detailed questioning. After half an hour the Committee on Reactor Safeguards ran out of questions. But the Jesuit Father had not given any signs of running out of answers. The session being at an end the expert, looking the chairman of the committee firmly in the eye and

[1] Dubbed by its friends "Committee for Reactor Prevention."
[2] One of the authors.

in a more authoritative voice than he had yet used, said, "Mr. Chairman, I can assure you on the highest authority that there will be no major earthquakes on Long Island in the next fifty years."

CHAPTER XVIII

By-products of Nuclear Reactors

NUCLEAR REACTORS generate energy with the help of nuclear fission. Every time a fission occurs we are left with radioactive by-products. It is most important to prevent the uncontrolled escape of these fission products from the reactor. Fortunately the dangerous products can be retained in the reactor—if the machine has been constructed and operated with reasonable care.

In the end, however, the burnt or partly burnt uranium charge will have to be removed from the reactor and fresh charge, fresh fuel will have to be added. What will become of the fission products at this time?

During protracted operation of a reactor most of the short-lived fission products decay. Those with longer lives accumulate. The discharge of the reactor is strongly radioactive, and it will remain radioactive for many years. One certainly must not dispose of this radioactive waste in a careless manner. There are, however, many ways in which one can store such waste with reasonable safety.

One can deposit the radioactive material in well-built underground tanks. One can concentrate the activity, imprison it in concrete blocks, and deposit it at the bottom of the ocean. If one is very much worried he might even put the radioactivity in rockets and let it decay harmlessly in outer space. These procedures will cost money and will add to the expense of nuclear energy.

It would be far better if we could find a way in which the radioactive by-products could be made to serve a useful and safe purpose. Some of the by-products can be used and have been used. These uses are connected with some hazards. Furthermore, only a small fraction of the fission products have found good employment up to the present. But the importance of fission products is growing.

We are using them in research. A radioactive isotope imitates the behavior of its non-active brother in all chemical reactions and in all the intricate processes in which matter changes its form inside a living body. Furthermore a radioactive substance can be detected with the greatest ease. It can be found in a concentration which is less than a millionth of a safe radiation dose. What the microscope has been in the exploration of the structure of organisms, the radioactive elements may become in the understanding of the chemical functioning of living matter.

With better understanding there comes the possibility of using radioactive by-products for diagnosis. As with the medical use of X-rays the possible small damage due to radiation exposure should be regarded as the price for the help we can get from early and correct recognition of diseases.

In the treatment of patients, particularly in the case of persons stricken by cancer, radioactive destruction of the diseased tissue is often preferable to the use of the surgeon's knife. Such radioactive treatment is new. There is much room for improvement. Appropriate use of radioactive substances for this purpose may become a far more powerful tool and much more widespread than it is at present.

But all these applications will use up only a vanishing

fraction of the fission products. Moreover, most of the biologically important elements are not produced in the fission of uranium. Many useful activities can be produced by neutron absorption in reactors. But among the fragments of uranium perhaps only radio-iodine has been put so far to direct physiological use.

Industry deals with less sensitive objects than living tissue. Therefore greater amounts of radioactive materials can be used here. And indeed radioactivity has done a great variety of jobs. The penetrating power of X-rays has been used to control the thickness of sheets in an easy and automatic manner. Radioactivity has been incorporated into surfaces which are exposed to mechanical wear or corrosion, to check the rate at which the surface is worn away by the appearance of activity in the lubricant or other fluids which have been in contact with the surface.

By such methods industry has accumulated savings which are rapidly approaching the billion dollar mark. These savings will increase as people learn how to use the new materials. But in all these cases it is important to make sure that the activity will not hurt anyone while it is used and after it has served its purpose.

Possibly the greatest amount of radioactivity will be needed in food sterilization and preservation. One may incorporate the activities into rods which will safely retain the materials but which will allow a considerable fraction of the penetrating gamma rays to escape.

To sterilize food means to destroy all microorganisms. Many of these are radiation-resistant and may have to be exposed to 50,000 or more roentgens—that is one hundred times as much as would kill a mammal.[1] Such massive irradiation

[1] This difference is not surprising. When we sterilize, we have to kill *all* germs, even those which are most resistant to radiation. Furthermore small organisms may escape the radiation effects by mere chance. On the other hand a big and complicated organism will cease to function when the most sensitive among its essential tissues have been destroyed.

begins to affect the foodstuff itself. In some cases sterilization by irradiation changes the food more than would be the case by boiling it or freezing it. In other cases irradiation produces less undesirable side effects than any other methods.

Another way to use radiation is the preservation of agricultural products. This need not be done by the difficult procedure of sterilization. It is enough to control pests and to prevent germination of the seeds which one is trying to preserve. Thus we need here approximately one per cent of the radiation that would be required for sterilization. By so little radiation the food is not altered to a noticeable extent. It is precisely in such processes, where great amounts of materials will have to be irradiated, that a substantial fraction of the fission products might find employment.

In all applications care has to be exercised lest radioactive materials should inadvertently be scattered around. Where great amounts are needed as in food sterilization and preservation, caution has to be redoubled. That trouble may arise has been illustrated by an occurrence in Houston, Texas.

Radioactive iridium[192], which is a beta and a gamma emitter, was being used by a certain industrial concern to take X-ray pictures of metal parts. A shipment of this radioactive material in the form of powder pellets was being opened by remote control when compressed gas in the container exploded and scattered some radioactivity around. The area was shielded but some of the radioactive dust escaped to the rest of the building. The two men who were operating the remote control apparatus became contaminated. They washed themselves and cleaned up the area but did not report the incident.

A few weeks later a standard radiation check showed that the plant was still radioactive. Company officials became worried and called in experts. At this late stage the plant was thoroughly decontaminated. The homes of the two men were also examined and were found to be slightly radioactive. The men and their families were temporarily moved out while their homes were being cleaned up. When they returned, neighbors and friends shunned them. The four year old son of one of the men lost his playmates. People were afraid to enter the houses. One of the houses was put up for sale but no one wanted to buy it.

The fact that the houses had been checked by radiation meters and found to be clean, and the fact that the half-life of iridium^{192} is only 75 days so that any trace of activity would disappear in a reasonably short time, did not dispel people's fears.

It is fortunate that no one was seriously hurt in this incident. But there is an important lesson we can learn from it: Ignorance may hurt more than radioactivity. That a house should lose its value in spite of the fact that its radioactive contamination has been removed, that a little boy should be shunned as though radioactivity were infectious like the plague—these are examples of suffering caused by one of the greatest sources of human misery: unreasoning fear.

The greatest potentialities of fission products for the future might lie in still a different direction. Radioactivity can induce mutations. To what extent this is a danger we have discussed in an earlier chapter. In the hands of a breeder who tries to bring about changes in animals or plants radioactivity could become exceedingly useful.

Of course it is true that most mutations are harmful. It is also true that artificial mutations have been produced for many decades. But now it is possible to place simple and cheap tools in the hands of many more people. Therefore the chances will increase to find among the many wrong mutations the few and decisive changes which lead to improvement.

Do we dare to place dangerous materials in so many hands? We should not do so without making certain that only competent and responsible individuals will get radioactive materials. This can be done. Druggists have dispensed poison; doctors and biologists have bred in their laboratories the multiplying menace of germs. All this was done and is being done with safety and to the great benefit of all people.

The use of radioactivity should be even more safe because this material is easy to detect. If poisons or germs become lost, they may be hard to find. Radioactive materials, however, give unmistakable evidence of their presence. It is, of course, never easy to find a needle in a haystack. But the chance to find it is much better if it is a radioactive needle.

Radioactive by-products need not remain what they seem to be today: dirt and danger to be disposed of and hidden. But in the immediate future we shall incur some expense to keep radioactivity in a safe place.

Some gaseous by-products like the long-lived krypton[85] (half-life: 10.4 years) might continue to give rise to real difficulties and to considerable expense. The trouble is, of course, that a noble gas like krypton will not be bound to any material by strong bonds. It may be inadvisable to let long-lived gases escape. On the other hand, their adsorption or their storage at low temperature or high pressure may prove to cost a considerable amount of money.

We have been talking about the problem of handling the by-products of nuclear power. This problem will not appear in proper proportion unless we also give some thought to the by-products of the kind of power we are using at present.

That we do not like smoke and smog is obvious. To what extent these residues of incomplete burning can cause cancer or other damage we do not know. Chemistry is more tricky than radiation. Our lack of knowledge about the slow biological effects of chemicals is much greater than our remaining uncertainties about radiation.

In addition to the obvious annoyance and worry caused by the products of incomplete combustion there exists an interesting question connected with the result of complete combustion. The carbon that has been deposited through the geologic ages as coal and as oil is being used up gradually and converted to a colorless, odorless, harmless gas—carbon dioxide. There is always some carbon dioxide in our atmosphere. The amount is approximately 300 parts per million of common air. All the carbon that has been burned since the beginning of the industrial revolution could have increased the carbon dioxide in the atmosphere by ten per cent to the value of 330 parts per million.

This increase could be significant. Carbon dioxide acts like a blanket or a valve for some kinds of radiation. In the daytime we receive energy in the form of visible light from the sun. This form of radiation has no difficulty in penetrating the carbon dioxide gas. However, the incoming radiation is balanced by invisible heat radiation, which flows out from the earth into space day and night. This infrared radiation is quite similar in nature to light, only our eyes are not sensitive to it. Now the carbon dioxide gas acts like a barrier, though only a partially effective barrier, to this outgoing heat radiation. If the carbon dioxide content of our atmosphere were to increase too greatly, it would act like the glass in a greenhouse and our climate would grow warmer.

A ten per cent increase in the carbon dioxide content of the atmosphere should have produced an observable rise in temperature. Such a temperature rise has not, in fact, been observed. The reason is that not all the carbon dioxide which has been generated in the processes of combustion has actually remained in the atmosphere. Most of it has found its way into the great reservoir of our oceans. Some of it is deposited as lime at the bottom of the oceans. However, some time is required for the carbon dioxide to be removed from the atmosphere and to reach the oceans. One would expect, therefore, that there would have been at least a slight increase in the carbon dioxide content of the atmosphere. Measurements show that this is the case and that the increase is about two per cent—which is too small to have changed our climate.

If we continue to consume fuel at an increasing rate, however, it appears probable that the carbon dioxide content of the atmosphere will become high enough to raise the average temperature of the earth by a few degrees. If this were to happen, the ice caps would melt and the general level of the oceans would rise. Coastal cities like New York and Seattle might be inundated.

Thus the industrial revolution using ordinary chemical fuel could be forced to end before the advantages of civilization have spread all over the earth. However, it might still be possible to use nuclear fuel. With nuclear fuel the industrial revolution and its countless benefits for man could continue to every part of the globe. The by-products of the nuclear age are less bulky and therefore are more easily handled than the by-products of our coal- and oil-economy. The main advantage of nuclear energy may yet turn out to be this: With proper care nuclear energy may turn out to be the cleanest among the available sources of power.

CHAPTER XIX

The Nuclear Age

THE FUTURE depends on people. People are unpredictable. Therefore, the future is unpredictable. However, some general conditions of mankind depend on things
like the development of technology, the control won by man
over nature and the limitations of natural resources. These
can be predicted with a little greater confidence. The future
is unknown but in some respects its general outline can be
guessed.

Such guesses are important. They influence our present
outlook and our present actions.

The nuclear age has not yet started. Our sources of energy
are not yet nuclear sources. Even in the military field, where
development has been most rapid, the structure of the armed
forces has not yet adjusted itself to the facts of the nuclear
age in a realistic manner. In politics the atomic nucleus has
entered as a promise and as a menace—not as a fact on which
we can build and with which we can reckon.

Some technical predictions seem safe:

Nuclear energy will not render our older power plants
obsolete in the near future. But nuclear energy will make it

possible to maintain the pace—even the acceleration—of the industrial revolution. It will be possible to produce all the energy we need at a moderate cost. Furthermore—and this is the important point—this energy will be available at any place on the globe at a cost which is fairly uniform. The greater the need for power, the sooner will it be feasible to satisfy the need with the help of nuclear reactors.

Nuclear energy can be made available at the most outlandish places. It can be used on the Antarctic continent. It can be made to work on the bottom of the ocean.

The expanding front of industrialization has been called the "revolution of rising expectations." That nuclear energy should be involved in the current and in the turbulence of this expanding front, is inevitable.

One can say a little more about the effects of scientific and technological discoveries on the relations among the people of the globe. With added discoveries raw materials will no longer be needed with the old urgency. For most substances substitutes are being found. This may make for greater economic independence.

On the other hand, new possibilities will present themselves. We shall learn how to control the air and how to cultivate the oceans. This will call for cooperation and more interdependence.

The dangers from radioactive by-products will act in a similar direction. The radioactive cloud released from a reactor accident may be more dangerous than a nuclear explosion. Such a cloud will not stop at national boundaries. Some proper form of international responsibility will have to be developed.

What effect the existence of nuclear weapons will have upon the coexistence of nations is a question less understood and less explored than any other affecting our future. Most people turn away from it with a feeling of terror. It is not easy to look at the question with calm reason and with little emotion.

A few predictions seem disturbing but are highly probable:

Nuclear secrets will not keep. Knowledge of nuclear weapons will spread among nations—at least as long as independent nations exist.

Prohibition will not work. Laws or agreements which start with the word "don't" can be broken and will always be broken. If there is hope, it must lie in the direction of agreements which start with the word "do." The idea of "Atoms for Peace" succeeded because it resulted in concrete action.

An all-out nuclear war between the major powers could occur but we may have good hope that it will not occur if we remain prepared to strike back. No one will want to provoke the devastation of his own country.

Atomic bombs may be used against cities. But there will be no military advantage in destroying cities. In a short and highly mobile war neither centers of supply and communication nor massive means of production will count. If cities are bombed, this will be done primarily for reasons of psychological warfare. We must be and we are prepared for this kind of war but only as a measure of retaliation. There is good reason to believe that as long as we are prepared for all-out war, our civilian population will not suffer from a nuclear attack.

The certainty of a counterblow gives real protection against all-out war. No such protection exists against wars limited in territory and in aims. In the history of mankind such wars have been most frequent. There is no indication that these limited wars have ended. We must be prepared for these conflicts with effective and mobile units, and this requires the use of nuclear firepower.

Nuclear weapons will certainly have a profound effect upon such limited warfare. Not all of this effect need be and indeed it must not be in the direction of greater devastation.

In a nuclear war it will not make sense to use massed manpower. Any such concentration will provide too good a target for atomic weapons. To use big, costly and conspicuous machines of war will be unwise. Such machines will be defeated by nuclear explosions in the same way as the mailed knight went down before firearms.

Any fighting unit in a nuclear war will have to be small, mobile, inconspicuous and capable of independent action. Such units whether on sea, land or in the air cannot rely and will not rely on fixed lines of supply. There will be no possibility and no need to occupy territory and to fight at fixed and definite fronts. If a war should be fought for military reasons and for military advantage, it will consist of short and sharp local engagements involving skill and advanced techniques and not involving masses that slaughter and are being slaughtered.

If an invader adopts extreme dispersion, it will become impossible to defeat him with atomic weapons. But a very highly dispersed army can be defeated by a determined local population. Therefore the main role of nuclear weapons might well be to disperse any striking force so that the resistance of people defending their homes can become decisive. Nuclear weapons may well become the answer to massed armies and may put back the power into the hands where we believe it belongs: the hands of the people.

At this point we are brought back to the main topic of this book: radioactivity. In a limited nuclear war the radioactive fallout will probably kill many of the innocent bystanders. We have seen that the testing program gives rise to a danger which is much smaller than many risks which we take in our stride without any worry. In a nuclear war, even in a limited one, the situation will probably be quite different. That noncombatants suffer in wars is not new. In a nuclear war, this suffering may well be increased further due to the radioactive poisons which kill friend and foe, soldier and civilian alike.

Fortunately there exists a way out. Our early nuclear explosives have used fission. In the fission process a great array of radioactive products are formed, some of them intensely poisonous. More recently we have learned how to produce energy by fusion. Fusion produces fewer and very much less dangerous radioactivities. Actually the neutrons which are a by-product of the fusion reaction may be absorbed in almost any material and may again produce an assortment of radioactive nuclei. However, by placing only certain materials near the thermonuclear explosion, one may obtain a weapon in which the radioactivity is harmless. Thus the possibility of clean nuclear explosions lies before us.

Clean, flexible and easily delivered weapons of all sizes would make it possible to use these bombs as we want to use them: as tools of defense. When stopping an aggressor we would not let loose great quantities of radioactive atoms which would spread death where we wanted to defend freedom. Clean nuclear weapons would be the same as conveniently packaged high explosives. They would be nothing more.

The possibility of clean explosions opens up another development: the use of nuclear explosives for the purposes of peace. Conventional high explosives have been used in peace fully as much as in war. From mining to the building of dams there is a great variety of important jobs that dynamite has performed. Nuclear explosives have not been used in a similar way. The reason is the danger from radioactivity. Once we fully master the art of clean explosions peaceful applications will follow and another step will be made in controlling the forces of nature.

All this is of course only a small part in the process of the increasing power of man and the increasing responsibility of man. As the impossible of yesterday becomes the accomplished fact of today we have to be more and more aware of our neighbors on this shrinking planet. The arts of peace may lead to conflicting interest as easily as they may lead to fruit-ful cooperation. If we ever learn to control the climate of the world, a nation may find itself in the same relation to another nation as two farmers who have to use the waters of the same river.

Rivals are men who fight over the control of a river. When the same word "rivals" comes to mean cooperation for the best common use of the river or any other resource—that will be the time of law and of peace. Surely this sounds like Utopia and no one sees the way. But the general direction in which we should go is not to consider atomic explosives and radioactivity as the inventions of the devil. On the contrary, we must more fully explore all the consequences and possi-bilities that lie in nature, even when these possibilities seem frightening at first. In the end this is the way toward a better life. It may sound unusually optimistic in the atomic age, but we believe that the human race is tough and in the long run the human race is reasonable.

GLOSSARY

Activity: Short for radioactivity. Also the strength of a radioactive source measured in disintegrations per second.

Air burst: A nuclear explosion at such an altitude that the fireball does not touch the earth's surface. An air burst produces very little local fallout.

Alpha ray (particle): Energetic but non-penetrating radiation emitted by heavy radioactive nuclei. An alpha particle consists of two neutrons and two protons, and is identical with the nucleus of the ordinary helium atom.

Atom: A positively charged nucleus surrounded by negatively charged electrons.

Atomic bomb: A fission bomb.

Atomic cloud: The cloud remaining after the energy of the explosion has been carried off by the shock wave and the thermal radiation. It consists of condensed water vapor, ground material, and bomb debris including the radioactivity.

Atomic energy: Energy released in nuclear reactions, for example in fission. Atomic energy and nuclear energy mean the same thing, but the latter name is more appropriate.

Atomic reactor: Same as nuclear reactor.

Background radiation: Natural radiation due to cosmic rays, and due to radioactive substances in the earth, in the atmosphere, and in our own bodies.

Beta ray (particle): An energetic electron or positron emitted by some radioactive nuclei. Practically all of the fission products are beta (electron) emitters.

Blast wave: Same as shock wave.

Cesium^{137}: A radioactive fission product. It emits a 0.5 million volt beta ray and a 0.7 million volt gamma ray with a half-life of 30 years. The daughter nucleus is stable barium^{137}.

Chain reaction: Self-maintained sequence of fissions. Neutrons released by the fission of one nucleus are used to induce fission in another nucleus.

Chromosome: A small irregularly shaped body found in cells. Chromosomes carry the genes, which are responsible for heredity.

Clean bomb: A nuclear bomb which produces heat and blast, but only a negligible amount of radioactivity. The energy of such a bomb is derived almost entirely from the fusion process.

Cobalt^{60}: Radioisotope—decays into nickel^{60} with the emission of a weak beta ray. The half-life for this decay is 5.3 years. The nickel^{60} immediately ejects two gamma rays with a total energy of 2.5 million electron-volts.

Cobalt bomb: A radiological bomb which produces a large quantity of cobalt^{60}.

Control rod: A rod of neutron-absorbing material used to control the power level of a nuclear reactor.

Cosmic rays: Energetic particles from outer space. They induce nuclear reactions in the earth's atmosphere and thus contribute to the background radiation. This cosmic radiation is more intense at high altitudes than at sea level.

Counter: A device which detects nuclear radiation.

Critical mass: The amount of fissionable material required to sustain a steady chain reaction. With less than the critical amount, the reaction stops because too many neutrons are lost.

Cyclotron: A machine that accelerates charged particles to high energy. Energetic charged particles can be used to induce nuclear reactions.

Daughter: The nucleus which remains after decay of a radioisotope.

Decay: Spontaneous process in which a radioactive nucleus emits an alpha, beta, or gamma ray.

Delayed neutrons: Those released after a fraction of a second to a half-minute or so by the fission products. They comprise less than one per cent of the total number of neutrons released in the fission process but are useful for the purpose of control in reactors.

Deuterium: Stable hydrogen isotope. Its nucleus (called a deuteron) consists of one proton and one neutron.

Disintegration: Same as decay.

Dose: A quantity of radiation—usually measured in roentgens.

$E = mc^2$: Einstein's equation relating mass (m) and energy (E). The speed of light (c) enters as a proportionality constant. The equation asserts that one pound of mass is equivalent to ten megatons of energy. In the fission process only one-tenth of one per cent of the mass is converted. Therefore, to produce ten megatons of energy by fission 1000 pounds of uranium would be required.

Electromagnetic radiation: Includes radio waves, visible, infrared, and ultraviolet waves; also X-rays and gamma rays. The latter two are energetic, penetrating forms of radiation.

Electron: A particle having a unit negative charge and a weight equal to 1/1840 of the weight of the lightest atom (hydrogen).

Electron capture: process in which an atomic electron unites with a proton in the nucleus producing a neutron and a neutrino.

Electron-volt: The amount of energy acquired by an electron which is accelerated through an electric potential of one volt. Typically, the energy required to "knock" an electron out of an atom is a few electron-volts or so; particles ejected from radioactive nuclei have energies between a few hundred thousand and a few million electron-volts.

Element: A collection of atoms whose nuclei all have the same charge. An element may consist of many isotopes.

Enriched material: Uranium which contains a greater proportion of the 235-isotope than is found in the natural ore.

Excited state: A state of an atom, molecule, or nucleus having excess energy. As soon as possible this excess energy is released and the system goes to the ground state.

Fallout: Radioactive particles from an atomic explosion. They may be carried in the atomic cloud to large distances from ground zero and then "rained down" to the earth's surface.

Fireball: The luminous ball of hot air and bomb material which expands and cools as the shock wave races out.

Fission: The breaking-up of a heavy nucleus into two or more fragments. A large amount of energy and some free neutrons are released in the process.

Fissionable material: Isotopes which undergo fission when bombarded by *slow* neutrons: uranium^{235} and plutonium^{239}.

Fission products: Fission fragments and their daughters, including hundreds of different radioactive species, among them strontium^{90} and cesium^{137}.

Fusion: The combining of light nuclei into heavier ones with a release of energy. For example, deuteron + triton ⟶ alpha + neutron. About 18 million electron-volts are released in this process.

Gamma ray: Energetic, penetrating electro-magnetic radiation emitted by certain radioactive nuclei, frequently after a beta emission.

Genes: Parts of the chromosomes. They are big molecules that determine heredity.

Ground state: The state of least energy and greatest stability of atoms, molecules, and nuclei.

Ground zero: The point on the surface of the earth directly above or below a nuclear explosion.

Half-life: The time required for one half of a large number of identical radioactive nuclei to disintegrate.

H-bomb: Same as hydrogen bomb.

Heavy hydrogen: Same as deuterium.

Heavy water: Water with heavy hydrogen substituted for ordinary hydrogen.

Hydrogen bomb: A high-yield thermonuclear bomb.

Iodine[131]: A radioactive fission product with a half-life of 8 days. It emits an electron of average energy 0.2 million electron-volts and a gamma ray of energy 0.4 million electron-volts.

Ion: A charged atom or molecule. Ions are produced in abundance when energetic charged particles pass through matter.

Ionization: The process of removing electrons from neutral atoms or molecules. Neutrons and gamma rays as well as energetic charged particles are very effective in producing ionization.

Iridium[192]: 75 day radioisotope. It emits an electron of average energy 0.2 million volts and a 0.3 million volt gamma ray.

Isotopes: Atoms whose nuclei have the same number of protons but a different number of neutrons. Such atoms have the same chemical behavior.

Kiloton: The amount of energy released by a thousand tons of TNT.

Krypton[85]: A radioactive fission product. It has a ten year half-life and emits an electron of average energy 0.2 million volts and a 0.5 million volt gamma ray.

Leukemia: A usually fatal disease in which white blood cells are overproduced.

Local fallout: Radioactive fallout in the neighborhood of a nuclear explosion.

Megaton: The amount of energy released by a million tons of TNT.

Meson: A particle intermediate in weight between the electron and the proton. Actually, there are two kinds of mesons, called pi and mu. The pi meson weighs 276 times as much as the electron and is connected with the forces that hold the nucleus together. The mu meson weighs 212 times as much as the electron and contributes appreciably to the cosmic radiation.

Microsecond: One millionth of a second. It takes light 5 microseconds to go a mile.

Million volt particle: Short for million electron-volt particle.

Moderator: A material used in nuclear reactors to reduce the speed of neutrons.

Molecule: A combination of atoms held together chemically.

Mutation: A genetic change, which is transmitted to offspring and affects hereditary characteristics. Such changes in genes may be caused by radiation as well as chemical and thermal agents.

Neutrino: A weightless, uncharged particle which carries off energy in the process of beta decay.

Neutron: A neutral particle, one of the basic constituents of the nucleus. A neutron weighs slightly more than a proton, and when free, decays into a proton plus an electron and a neutrino.

Noble gases: Helium, neon, argon, krypton, and xenon. They do not combine chemically with any elements including themselves.

Nuclear bomb: A bomb which derives its energy from nuclear fission or fusion.

Nuclear reactor: A machine for maintaining a controlled chain reaction.

Nucleus: The core of an atom, consisting of neutrons and protons. Its charge is equal to the number of protons. Its weight is equal to the number of protons plus the number of neutrons.

Periodic system: The chemical elements arranged in order of increasing atomic charge. Elements with similar chemical properties occur periodically.

Plutonium: Element with charge 94, produced by capturing a neutron in uranium^{238} followed by two beta emissions. Like uranium^{235}, plutonium is valuable as an atomic fuel.

Positron: The positive counterpart of the electron.

Potassium^{40}: A natural radioactive isotope. It has a half-life of one billion years and emits beta and gamma rays.

Proton: A constituent of the nucleus. It has one unit of positive charge and weighs slightly less than a neutron.

Radiation: Energetic charged particles, neutrons and gamma rays which cause ionization in matter. Radiation is produced in nuclear explosions but also occurs naturally from cosmic rays and from the decay of radioactive substances in our surroundings.

Radioactivity: Spontaneous nuclear decay, releasing an alpha, beta, or gamma ray.

Radioisotope: Short for radioactive isotope.

Radiological bomb: A bomb designed to create radioactive contamination.

Radium: Element with charge 88. The principal isotope has a weight of 226 and emits an alpha particle with a half-life of 1620 years.

Range: Distance traveled by an energetic charged particle in matter before it stops. Heavy charged particles move in a straight line inside matter, but electrons frequently change their course. For this reason the range of electrons is only about one-half the total distance traveled.

Reactor: Same as nuclear reactor.

Roentgen: A measure of radiation dose—defined in terms of the amount of energy deposited per unit weight of irradiated material. A dose of 400,000 roentgens in living tissue deposits enough energy to raise the temperature by $1°$ C. A dose of only 400 roentgens in a human being will cause death fifty per cent of the time.

Shock wave: Expanding front of high pressure and strong winds produced by an explosion.

Spontaneous fission: Natural fission, not induced by a neutron. The half-life for this process in uranium^{238} is 8×10^{15} years.

Stratosphere: The atmosphere above the weather zone. The altitude of the stratosphere varies from thirty to fifty thousand feet depending on latitude and season.

Stratospheric fallout: World-wide fallout from big bombs whose clouds rise into the stratosphere. On the average the radioactivity remains in the stratosphere for about ten years and is then deposited more or less uniformly over the surface of the earth.

Strontium^{90}: A radioactive fission product. It has a half-life of 28 years and emits two electrons of average total energy 1.2 million electron-volts. Strontium is chemically similar to calcium and gets deposited in bones.

Thermal radiation: Electromagnetic radiation, mainly visible, but also ultraviolet and infrared, emitted from the fireball of a nuclear explosion and transmitted long distances in the surrounding cold air.

Thermonuclear bomb: A bomb which derives a significant fraction of its energy from the fusion of hydrogen isotopes.

Thermonuclear reaction: A fusion reaction induced by high temperature.

Thorium: Element with charge 90. The principal isotope has a weight of 232 and emits an alpha particle with a half-life of 14 billion years.

Trigger process: A small cause which leads to a big effect.

Tritium: An isotope of hydrogen. Its nucleus (called a triton) consists of one proton and two neutrons. Tritons are radioactive beta emitters having a half-life of 12.25 years.

Troposphere: The weather portion of the atmosphere, from sea level to about forty thousand feet.

Tropospheric fallout: World-wide fallout, mainly from small bombs (less than a megaton) whose clouds remain in the troposphere. This fallout occurs on the average two weeks to a month after the explosion and stays in a latitude close to the latitude of the explosion.

Uranium: Element with charge 92. Natural uranium contains 1 part of U^{235} to 139 parts of U^{238}. U^{235} is a fissionable material and U^{238} can be converted to plutonium, which is fissionable.

X-ray: Penetrating electromagnetic radiation, usually made by bombarding a metal target with energetic electrons. X-rays and gamma rays are really the same thing.